# Robert Bakewell and
# the Longhorn Breed of Cattle

# Robert Bakewell and the Longhorn Breed of Cattle

*Pat Stanley*

*FARMING PRESS*

*For my father*

First published 1995

ISBN 0 85236 305 2

A catalogue record for this book is available
from the British Library

**Published by Farming Press Books**
**Wharfedale Road, Ipswich IP1 4LG, United Kingdom**

Distributed in North America
by Diamond Farm Enterprises,
Box 537, Alexandria Bay, NY 13607, USA

*Front cover photographs*
*Top* 'Robert Bakewell at Dishley Grange' by John Boultbee
(Royal Agricultural Society of England)

*Bottom* 'Prize Livestock at Dishley Grange' by Thomas Weaver, 1802
(Iona Antiques, London)

Cover design by Mark Beesley
Typeset by Galleon Typesetting
Printed and bound in Great Britain by Butler & Tanner, Frome and London

# Contents

THERE IS A COLOUR SECTION FOLLOWING PAGE 134

# Acknowledgements

I would like to thank many people for their help and encouragement in the making of this book, but especially:

- J. H. S. Thompson FRICS, chief land agent to the Fitzwilliam Estates.
- M. J. Rogers FRICS, former chief land agent to the National Trust.
- The National Trust, Calke Abbey, Derbyshire (Mr K. Usher, administrator).
- I. G. & J. E. Mattley, Phenotype Books, Penrith, Cumbria.
- The Royal Agricultural Society of England and their librarian at the National Agricultural Centre, Stoneleigh, Philip Sheppey.
- John Heathcote Ball.
- Jim Beechey.
- Rita Callwood.
- Geoff and Judith Gilby.
- Dick and Claire Clarke.
- Miss A. Harpur Crewe.
- Iona Antiques, London.
- Graftons of Market Harborough.
- My publishers Farming Press: Roger Smith, Julanne Arnold, and all their staff.
- Kay Edge for her editorial help.
- David Edgar for his many valuable suggestions.
- And finally, the three men in my life, John, Ben and Joe, for their tolerance and understanding.

# Introduction

Even in these increasingly urban times, almost everyone has heard of Robert Bakewell (1725–95). He was the great improver of farm livestock and he still finds a place in most school history books, with Jethro Tull (seed drills), Turnip Townshend (Norfolk four-course rotation) and Coke of Norfolk, later Lord Leicester of Holkham. Along with collaborators and rivals in their day, these great men of British farming showed the way to expand agricultural production which, with gradually increasing food imports over most of the period, enabled the British population to increase from 7 million in 1760 when food imports were virtually nil to 30 million in 1881 when food imports from the New World became a major factor.

Jethro Tull (1674–1741) showed the way to grow heavier yields of traditional crops; Turnip Townshend (1674–1738) increased the total production of land over a rotation even if at least two of his four crops – wheat, roots (turnips), barley and seeds (hay) – had to be processed through animals to be of value to man; Bakewell provided the improved livestock to process the crops for human use; and Coke of Norfolk (1752–1842) brought all these elements together in his new commercial farming. More or less.

Robert Bakewell is best remembered for developing the New Leicester Sheep, the breed claimed to have been infused into virtually every one of the 40 or more native British sheep breeds, and many abroad. Leicesters are also a more direct parent of breeds such as the Hexham or Bluefaced Leicester and the Border Leicester, which are themselves of major significance in the cross-bred lambs they produce out of yet other breeds – the Swaledale, the Cheviot, the Blackface and many more. In one way or another, the Leicester is also closely related to other large longwoolled breeds – the Wensleydale, the Lincoln Longwool and the Cotswold, for example.

Longhorn cattle, another of the major breeds on which Bakewell worked, have had a more mixed reception down the years. The Longhorn was eclipsed soon after Bakewell's death, and this was, to an extent, Bakewell's own fault. For it seems that he so stimulated thinking about cattle breeding that farmers improved the fairly new Shorthorn so greatly and rapidly that by early in the 20th century the Longhorn was considered to be of no more than historical interest. Yet the Longhorn survives and is increasing in response to new or revised ideas on cattle breeding and beef production as we move towards the 21st century.

There is always an element of stubbornness in any farmer who maintains a breed which is not the most popular of its day. Yet there are a number of characteristics which make the Longhorn attractive even in the 1990s, and after three decades of beef breeds being imported from Europe and elsewhere. One is its docility, noted by virtually all its breeders who are, in any case, not likely to keep a wild breed with horns such as the Longhorn has. Another is its record of easy calving, an important feature for any farmer who will almost certainly have a large number of other chores and has no wish to miss his sleep.

A third characteristic of merit is that the Longhorn appears to thrive even on relatively poor-quality grassland such as that in which rock or other factors make it difficult to plough and improve the quality of the sward. Fourth, and by no means least, the Longhorn does seem to have a large percentage of lean meat in its carcase and therefore commends itself to modern Jack Spratt consumers.

Mrs Pat Stanley is, with her husband John, a breeder of Longhorn cattle on a farm in the Charnwood Forest area of Leicestershire. This forest area was a major cradle of the breed as it came into recorded history in the early 1700s. It is also an area on the edge of which the great Robert Bakewell farmed, at Dishley on the outskirts of Lough-borough, and was also home to some of his collaborating and rival farmers. Moreover, Pat Stanley grew up on a neighbouring farm on the Calke Estate, in south Derbyshire, which has made its own considerable mark on the history of the Longhorn.

Her method has been to absorb, over many years, all the traditions, written and otherwise, of this great breed of the English Midlands and she here reproduces many of the major writings about the breed over the years, interspersed with her own comments. In doing so she has created what is a substantial history of the Longhorn breed and a new interpretation of the work of master breeder Robert Bakewell.

Her story is of major interest not only in its discussion of breeding and feeding cattle and other livestock but also in the comments which flow from years past on the issues of the day as seen by the writers she quotes, or from their subjects whom they quote. Attitudes to farm workers, to rural transport and to religion as it affected people at the grass roots all have something to offer to the social historian. Some of the language of earlier writings, and the art of 'likenesses' at various times, provide yet more interest in her work.

Pat Stanley focuses at one point on the extra meat that Bakewell's ideas produced for a population that consequently had the nutrition from which to grow. The master historian of *English Farming, Past and Present*, Lord Ernle, made a similar point about the 18th century: 'a time rapidly approaching when beef and mutton were to be more important than the power of draught and the fineness of wool. Bakewell was the agricultural opportunist who saw the impending change and knew how it should be met. By providing meat for the millions, he contributed as much to the wealth of the country as Arkwright or Watt. There is some foundation for the statement that many monuments have been reared in Westminster Abbey to the memory of men who less deserved the honour than Robert Bakewell.'

This book should go some way to reminding us of the important contribution made to the development of the British nation by Bakewell, and by many of his contemporaries who are also discussed.

C. DAVID EDGAR

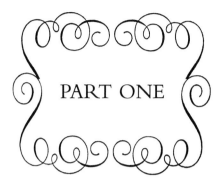

PART ONE

# Robert Bakewell of Dishley Grange

*Robert Bakewell (from an engraving by F. Englehart, after the painting by Boultbee).*

# CHAPTER ONE

# Robert Bakewell, Farmer and Innovator

Leicestershire lays claim to a full share of celebrity for being the cradle and nursery of some of the great modern improvements in Agriculture. These improvements, more especially those connected with the breeding of animals, were in a great degree projected and executed by Robert Bakewell, whose talents burst the fetters of rustic ignorance and long established usage; who exalted the ordinary drudgery of ordinary cultivation into the dignity of a science of the highest national benefit and importance, and discovered and demonstrated the principles by which form, size, strength and beauty of our most useful farm animals may be brought to the highest perfection.

He seems to have solved that difficult and valuable problem by what means the maximum of wholesome and nutritious food can be obtained for the use of man in the shortest space of time and on the minimum vegetable substance.

*(Local directory, 1860)*

On 23 May 1725, a son was born to Robert and Rebecca Bakewell of Dishley Grange near Loughborough, Leicestershire, whose life and deeds were to have far-reaching and everlasting effects on agriculture worldwide. The child, the third Robert Bakewell of Dishley, was to become one of the most important agriculturists of all time. He was truly unique. The like of such men as he number but few in our great history, for his ideas were original and very much in advance of his time.

3

His early manhood was spent, with every encouragement from his forward-thinking father, travelling both in this country and abroad, absorbing knowledge like a sapling oak taking up nourishment from the earth to produce a king among trees. His thirst for knowledge remained unquenched throughout his life. He was a man of great qualities, amongst which were to be found in abundant quantity enthusiasm, perseverance, observation, judgement and, above all, great kindness to both men and beasts.

Bakewell was to provide the answer to the increased food demand which was an integral part of the Industrial Revolution, often held to have started in the year he took over Dishley Grange from his father, 1760. His objective was to improve every class of farm livestock, providing the nation with animals exclusively for meat rather than what had been available up to that time, namely aged draught animals retiring from the yoke.

Although his greatest success was to be with sheep, untold numbers of which were touched by the Dishley blood, no history of Longhorn cattle would be complete without the story of the man who was justly named by J. Neville Fitt in 1876 as their 'Great High Priest'.

Bakewell was the descendant of a very old and highly respected family, the tree of which could be traced for 600 years from Leverretus, thane of the King and the King's chancellor in the reign of Henry II. Leverretus was presented with the rectory of Bakewell in Derbyshire in 1158, making the initial link with what was to be adopted as the family name. Three consecutive descendants were rectors of Bakewell until the last, on his retirement from the parish in the reign of King John, retained the territorial name and so became the founder of the family line. Down through the ages, the family was able to boast a baron of the Exchequer, two members of Parliament and a foreign ambassador. We are therefore looking at a man who came from no ordinary background.

In 1693 Bakewell's grandfather took Dishley on a 99-year lease from Sir Ambrose Phillips. Bakewell's grandfather (1643–1716) was the first of three Robert Bakewells of Dishley. The second (1685–1773) had, according to the obituary notice in the *Gentleman's Magazine*, 'the reputation of being one of the most ingenious and able farmers of the neighbourhood' and it is from

QUADRUPEDS
BOS TAURUS, OXEN.

Long Horned or Lancashire Breed.

*Longhorn bull and cow from an old undated engraving.*

him that Robert III, our Robert Bakewell, gained much of his pioneering spirit and enterprise. In 1809 the agricultural writer William Pitt remarked that 'Bakewell was encouraged by his father beyond all parallel and without limitation.' It can therefore be concluded that Bakewell served a sound apprenticeship under the guiding hand of his very able father until, at the age of 35, he took over total responsibility for the running of the farm and from then on became increasingly famous beyond the boundaries of Leicestershire for his revolutionary methods of agriculture and superior specimens of farm livestock.

His holding, when visited by Arthur Young in 1770, was of 440 acres, 110 of which were arable and the rest in grass. The arable usually included 15 acres of wheat, 25 acres of spring corn and 30 acres of turnips. On this acreage he ran 60 horses, 400 large sheep and 160 cattle of all sizes and various breeds.

Mr R. E. Prothero (later Lord Ernle, 1851–1937) described Bakewell as resembling the typical yeoman who figured on Staffordshire pottery, 'a tall, broad-shouldered man, of brown red complexion, clad in loose brown coat and scarlet waistcoat, leather breeches and top boots'. This complements very well the image we have of Bakewell sitting astride his horse at Dishley as portrayed by the 18th-century artist John Boultbee (see front cover).

Writing in 1805, John Lawrence said that 'Bakewell had a kind face which showed a combination of intelligence and shrewdness. His manners had a rustic yet polite and pleasing frankness. He spoke with economy, and always to the point, and had a store of anecdotes and stories.' As to any political leanings, Bakewell had none, but Lawrence adds that 'He lived and died one of the warmest supporters and staunchest defenders of liberty.'

Dishley Church, the first written mention of which was in 1220, by the Bishop of Lincoln, was, and is, within the Dishley Grange grounds. It had never been very flourishing, and services were held there infrequently. Bakewell therefore followed his parents to the Unitarian Chapel on Warners Lane in nearby Loughborough, which was built in 1743. He became a trustee, like his father, in 1774, and in 1761 was also made a trustee of Mountsorrel Chapel, near Loughborough. Even throughout his later financial embarrassment he continued with monetary assistance to these chapels. Religion was a serious part of his life and he would never conduct business on a Sunday, regardless of how important a visitor might be or how far they might have travelled.

Later, when he formed the Dishley Society, it was written into the rules that no member could show rams on a Sunday.

Anyone visiting Dishley was shown most generous hospitality, the door being always open to friends and strangers alike when they shared in Bakewell's passion for the progression of agriculture.

His household was run for him by his capable sister, Hannah, who never married and predeceased him in 1793 at the age of 60 years. Hannah's domain, the great Mecca to which all agricultural students and enthusiasts flocked, including 'Russian princes, French and German royal dukes, British peers and sightseers of every degree', was a building of ancient construction. Illustrations of it appear in the background of some of the paintings of Bakewell's prize animals by John Boultbee.

*Dishley Grange as it looked in 1790.*

One such view, when enlarged from a late 18th-century engraving, appears to show two parallel blocks of buildings on either side of a yard. The further or northern block looks to be of medieval origin, showing narrow, possibly lancet windows. The engraver has made no attempt to hatch the walls, as in the brick end of the timbered southern block, which could lead to the assumption that it was stone built. The massive end chimney indicates an original use as a brew house, laundry or something similar, when occupied as a principal grange to Garendon Abbey.

Following the dissolution of the monasteries in 1539, the grange buildings, like many others, were used for farming purposes, the lack of a farmhouse being overcome by the adaptation of the bailiff's quarters, or domestic buildings, which were easily converted. The curious curved structure at the eastern end, as yet unexplained, may be represented by an existing single storey building with a bowed end, standing, as near as can be judged, in the same position, with a long stone wall, which may be the rear wall of the northern block.

Surely this must be Robert Bakewell's house, the home of several generations of the Bakewell family, a fact borne out by its inclusion in the landscapes of his animal portraits? The substantial-looking building had obviously been adapted over the 200 years since its monastic ownership, and its close proximity to the farm buildings made it ideal for overseeing the farmyard and the animals. Additions had been made at various stages of its life for the convenience of the occupants, giving it a look lacking regularity and compactness, but lending it a naive style, which gave it a pastoral simplicity and charm.

However, very little structural evidence from Bakewell's time has survived. His dovecote, capable of housing up to 640 pairs of birds, still stands guard over Bakewell's final resting place, along with other members of his family, inside the tiny, ruined Dishley Church. Of the farm buildings, only a couple of examples which would have been standing during his life are still in existance. Most of the others were probably demolished during a period of agricultural prosperity in the 1850s and their materials reused in a programme of modernisation. Further buildings were lost in the 1960s.

J. Neville Fitt, writing in 1876, portrayed a most poignant scene: 'Not long ago I chanced to be in the neighbourhood of Dishley, and I turned aside to see the grave of the man who had done so much for the peaceful industry of his country. I found it in the little, unused and dilapidated church close to the Grange, where his princely hospitality was dispensed, now only a dovecote and a building place for the fowls of the air.'

Bakewell was surround by faithful servants who had been with him many years, some of them from his father's time. One of his principles was that he would not employ anyone for a period of less than four years, at the end of which time it was rarely found that anyone would desire to leave. The minimum four-year term of service imposed by Bakewell upon members of staff may have been a contributory factor in the prevention of the secrets of his breeding policy becoming common knowledge. A contented and happy worker naturally becomes attached and loyal to his employer and an honest one will never betray a trust that has been shown to him.

Bakewell's animals were renowned for their extreme docility, probably in response to the kind treatment they received at Dishley. In 1771 Arthur Young described with amusement the way in which bulls would just stand still in the field to be examined by visitors: 'A lad with a stick three feet long, and as big as his finger, will conduct a bull, away from his companions, and guide him from one end of the farm to the other. All this gentleness is merely the effect of management, and the mischief often done by bulls is undoubtedly owing to practices very contrary, or else to a total neglect.'

In 1790 William Marshall gave another account of the Long-horn bulls which, although of frightening size and appearance, were so gentle they could be, and were, handled by children – one even submitting to being ridden. 'At an age when most of his brethren are either foaming or bellowing with rage and madness, Old C, a bull, had all the gentleness of a lamb, both in his look and action. He would lick the hand of his feeder and, if petted or scratched, would bow himself down almost to his knees.'

John Lawrence, writing in 1805, related that he'd heard it said that 'One of Bakewell's work bulls was in the constant habit of dragging a cart by himself, without a driver, to a brewhouse two miles distant and returning home with a load of grains.' This is the only reference I have found inferring that Bakewell used bulls for draught. It may have been just one incident of an exceptionally quiet animal having been used for this purpose so many times he was able to complete the trip unaided. There are many instances of horses behaving in this way. No doubt we have all heard the

*Engravings by Garrard of Mr Honeybourne's New Leicester bull and cow of pure Dishley breeding.*

many old stories of horses returning their owners to their homes after too much ale had been consumed!

This was all in complete contrast to the behaviour usually shown to animals at this period. Bakewell was always outraged when he witnessed the commonplace acts of cruelty perpetrated against all forms of farm livestock at the time. Drovers travelling the country, taking animals to markets and fairs, were considered to be amongst the foremost culprits. This behaviour was for the most part ignored by a population whose own lives were hard and living conditions intolerable without wasting their thoughts and time on the suffering of 'dumb' animals.

Marshall further remarked that Bakewell was the only person of his acquaintance to leave calves on their mothers, a practice which had the effect of quick growth. 'The growth of calves reared in this way is strikingly rapid.' Here we see Bakewell leading the field by giving his cattle a good start in life, not only with the milk of the dam but also by providing calves with extra feed which they obtained from mobile creep feeders which he devised.

What a marked difference there must have been between Bakewell's and the neighbouring stock. On the one hand, pedigree animals on well-managed pasture with supplementary feeding, and on the other local mongrel cattle on unimproved pastures, generally foraging for themselves. Not only was Bakewell paying particular attention to his animals' hereditary make-up, but also to their growth and well-being in the initial stages of life.

Bakewell's quest for knowledge led him down every avenue of agriculture. In order to improve his livestock he also had to improve the land from which they were fed, and in order to improve the land he utilised both manure and irrigation. In his early years, when stock were housed, little if any use was made of bedding or litter. Instead, his animals, which were kept tied, were fed little but often to keep their appetites keen, with all forage going through their systems and not on to the floor as bedding. This naturally produced very rich manure, the making of which Bakewell believed was one of the most important points of husbandry.

He was so convinced of the superior value of manure produced in this way, as opposed to that of loose-housed animals in bedded yards, that he would take in neighbouring stock over the winter months of November to March, providing he had room for them, his only return being the dung they produced.

Arthur Young tells us that 'it was the method of many farmers to run their cattle out all winter, with the fodder stacks round about them. This was a most erroneous way. The land was badly poached. The stacks were destoyed, causing great wastage, and the valuable dung was scattered thinly over the field.' Otherwise they were kept in yards open to the elements, with access to fodder round the sides.

Bakewell could, and did, winter up to 170 cattle all tied in standings which he devised, and had built into purpose-made sheds or old barn conversions. This was all done at his own expense and not that of his landlord. The standings he created were to aid the easy retrieval of dung and to reduce wastage of this most valuable product. For many years, he maintained that manure increased its fertilising power with age and that it should be kept at least three years before use until it had the consistency of peat dust. (He later changed this opinion, however.)

The floors of the standings where the beasts stood were paved, and were 6–8 in. higher than the level of the barn floor. They were just broad enough for a beast to stand on, though with some difficulty, the result being that all the dung fell beyond the standing and into the lower channel. When the beast lay down it drew itself up onto the higher standing and in this way was elevated above the dung, keeping quite clean without the need of litter. A man was employed to keep the channels clean and barrow the dung to a central clamp in the open yard which was sur-rounded by the cattle sheds. (Bakewell's design of cow standings is not so different from the continuing discussion of recent years on the dimensions for cow cubicles for dairy animals.)

By not utilising straw for litter, but keeping it all for forage, he was able to greatly reduce his winter feed bill. Large quantities of hay were produced from his water meadows and the means for maintaining his stock were also increased by the cultivation of vetches, turnips*, cabbage, carrots and potatoes. Other crops tried were coleseed and borecole. Carrots, although expensive, were

---

* The first reference to turnips being eaten by sheep is in *Houghton's Collections on Husbandry and Trade*, a periodical work begun in 1681.

highly valued as stock feed. They were preserved in various ways through the winter, some being buried in earth, while others were stored in buildings. Tops and roots were fed when fresh, but after storage the tops were removed. Potatoes were used when the price was low, and coleseed was sown into oat stubble for use by sheep, when it had grown a sufficient bulk of leaf in the period from late autumn to early spring.

It was with resources such as these that Bakewell managed to support such large numbers of animals on a limited acreage.

Near to his house Bakewell had several small plots of grassland of less than an acre in size, which were kept very well fenced. These were used for isolating small lots of cattle or sheep. The rest of the farm was divided into 10 acre closes. These divisions were carried out by Bakewell at his own expense, even though a tenant of the farm, and were mainly created by growing hawthorn hedges, back-fenced against the animals (see p. 146).

He also put in large plantations of white willow (*Salix alba*) which, when mature, were used for gates, hurdles, fence rails and other purposes. His famous chair, which is held by the Royal Agricultural Society of England, was made from willow grown on his farm. It is from this chair that he is said to have held court in his kitchen at Dishley, and at night would have been found writing up the day's proceedings, settled in its welcome embrace. The R.A.S.E. journal of 1896 recorded that Bakewell's chair was presented to the Society by one of its members, Mr Henry C. Woodcock of Rearsby, Leics., and that it was accompanied by a painting representing Bakewell on horseback.

One stand of willow was planted almost the full length of the canal which he constructed through his farm, while several plantations were situated near to the house and buildings. These were cut in a seven-year rotation.

He reinforced all his gates with cross-footed hurdles made from willow to prevent them being forced by any strong and determined animal. Obviously this was a circumstance brought about by the large number of males kept. All the trimmings from the willow, when producing these various articles, were used as a base for straw and hay ricks.

In 1770 Arthur Young described the irrigation methods used by Bakewell at Dishley as 'among the rarest instances of spirited

*Bakewell's chair.*

husbandry' and Marshall classed him as 'standing first in the kingdom as an improver of grassland by watering'. From Monk's *Agricultural Report* we find that Bakewell was able to cut grass four times a year after growing it by means of irrigation. Originally 60–80 acres at Dishley gained considerable benefit from natural flooding by the River Soar, but after a trip to the west of England to study irrigation methods, accompanied by a Mr George Boswell who had published a book on the subject entitled *A Treatise on Watering of Meadows, Low Lands Etc.*, Bakewell proceeded to irrigate a further 100 acres of his land artificially.

On his return from this fact-finding mission, Bakewell put his genius to work by diverting for his needs the 'Blackbrook', a small water course which skirted the farthest boundary of his farm. He changed its path at the highest point he could and carried it, by means of a freshly cut canal of one-and-a-quarter miles in length, not only around the higher points of the land available for the scheme on his farm, but also to supply the farmstead with water. As well as a multitude of other purposes to which it was put, he was able to create a drinking pool for livestock and a wash pool for his sheep.

The 100 acres of his newly converted water meadows were originally in ridge and furrow, as was most of the county. Bakewell ploughed this up and cultivated and reseeded it, leaving grassland with a perfectly even surface. Then, by means of ditches known as floats, he conveyed water from his newly constructed canal, causing the water to flow over the land at will. Water was returned to the canal by drains or sumps.

While this operation was in progress the whole surface area to be flooded was covered with a sheet of water at least an inch in depth. In very hot weather it was allowed to lie for up to 48 hours, in moderate weather for 4–5 days and when cold for up to 14 days. If there was a possibility of frost the operation was stopped.

Always one to be sure of his facts, Bakewell devised experimental plots to establish the validity of his methods. One plot would be flooded, another not; a further plot would be manured, while yet another would be irrigated with spring water and another flooded with canal water. In this way he could compare the value of irrigation against other forms of fertiliser, and also the different methods of irrigation.

'Our farmer', Young remarked, 'has expended large sums in these uncommon undertakings; he richly deserves the enjoyment of their profit.' The difference in the colour of the grass on the watered and unwatered land was said to be 'astonishing', and the amount of grass produced on the watered area was in the proportion of 10 to 1 against the unwatered sickly, yellow grass. Neighbouring land remained full of great quantities of rushes and coarse, sour grass, while Bakewell's land was so well tended it was almost free from weeds. Young reported that, prior to Bakewell improving his land by the creation of new water meadows, it had been in a state similar to that of the rest of the county, covered in ant hills and disfigured by irregularities of surface. His neighbours are said to have looked upon his grassland operations with horror, feeling that the ploughing was 'burying good land to bring up bad'.

Fearful that his flood water should overflow their land and 'poison it', some people actually started legal proceedings against him to stop the work. Agreement seems to have been reached by Bakewell undertaking to construct banks to prevent the water straying off his own farm.

Bakewell used the spoil thrown up by cleaning out his local Blackbrook to fill in the hollows along its course and he kept both the brook and its tributary ditches clean and repaired. He extended his original 60 acres of naturally flooded meadows gradually, feeling his way gently and experimenting constantly to prove to himself the efficiency and economy of the system.

Another purpose to which he turned his canal was to use it as a cheap and easy means of moving his crops of turnips and cabbages from the fields to the buildings, and manure from the buildings to the fields. He designed a flat-bottomed boat for this purpose but, finding it not the easiest thing to use, he hit upon the simple idea of throwing the turnips straight into the water and allowing them to float down to the barn. In 1789 he designed a reservoir for them to fall into, with a grate at the bottom to release the water but retain the turnips. They came out beautifully clean and ready to be stored for the winter.

The canal he cut was narrow and, of course, had a minimum fall but the actual reduction in labour costs, both human and animal, in using the waterway for conveying root crops, etc. was said to be 'huge'.

Remarkable though it may seem, evidence still remains of Bakewell's revolutionary irrigation system, although it is well over 200 years since it was installed. Timber liners of elm for the canal and brickwork drainage wells still survive to help us piece together this man's great achievement.

# CHAPTER TWO

# Bakewell and the New Leicester Sheep

The breed is originally Lincolnshire but Mr Bakewell thinks, and very justly, that he has much improved it.

(*Arthur Young, 1771*)

Robert Bakewell's greatest and most lasting achievement must be his development of the Dishley or New Leicester sheep. The origin of this animal was described by both Arthur Young and George Culley as being of a Lincolnshire variety. Indeed, Culley, who was Bakewell's first pupil, had monitored them from their beginnings and closely followed their development.

Mr Ferryman, who spoke to many of Bakewell's contempories, said that 'Bakewell had formed in his own mind an ideal perfection, which he endeavoured to realise, and that with this view he, with unwearied perseverance, year after year, and at something more than market price, selected from the flocks around him such ewes as possessed points, which were most likely to produce the animal he wished for.'

David Lowe wrote in 1842 that Bakewell himself told Mr Chaplin, an 'Old Lincolnshire' breeder, that at one time he had used Old Lincolnshire rams. From a speech given by Sir John Sinclair, president of the first Board of Agriculture, to the Society for the Improvement of British Wool at Edinburgh in January 1791 we are told that all the large breeds of English sheep were of recent introduction, within half a century before that date. If so, they were newly imported or newly developed breeds when

Bakewell began his work of improvement.

But Gervase Markham wrote in 1614 that Leicestershire sheep were 'large boned and of good shape. . . . Old Leicester was large, heavy and coarse-woolled, giving a 15-in. fleece of up to 12 lb in weight.' Markham also said that Lincolnshire had the largest sheep. Lisle, writing in 1757 in reference to the 17th century, gave a warning to the effect that only a 'lesser size' of Lincoln tup should be used on ewes to avoid excessively large lambs.

However, in *Like Engendering Like*, written by Nicholas Russell in 1986, the view is expressed that large sheep may indeed have been introduced to this country not long before Bakewell's time, as suggested by Sinclair. Any previous progress to that of Bakewell must be accredited to Joseph Allom, reported by William Marshall as being of Clifton, Notts. After starting in farming as a ploughboy, Allom, through sheer hard work, became one of the best-known sheep breeders prior to Bakewell. Two conflicting theories of the origin of Allom's sheep say that he bought them at a Lincolnshire market or, the idea more favourably looked upon, that he purchased them mostly from a Mr Stone of 'Godeby' near Melton Mowbray. In Allom's day it was certainly customary for the superior farmers to purchase their ram lambs from him for between 2 and 3 guineas.

Although the first few steps down the long road to improvement may have been taken by Allom, it was actually Bakewell's ability and perseverance which won the day. The way in which this achievement came about caused great debate at the time amongst the very top people of the agricultural profession. Different suggestions were made regarding the breeds of sheep Bakewell was thought to have used, but Marshall implies that there was no other ingredient in their making other than his total belief in the use of breeding in-and-in, using the best specimens of one breed.

It is interesting to study and compare the descriptions of the Dishley sheep given by two highly competent men, namely William Marshall and George Culley.

Marshall, writing a description of Bakewell's superior ewes and wethers in top condition, said that their heads were long but small and hornless, with the ears somewhat long and standing backwards, and the nose shooting forward. The neck was thin and clean towards the head, but taking a conical form, standing low and enlarging every way at the base. The fore-end was altogether short, the bosom broad and the shoulder, ribs and chine exceedingly full. The loin was broad and the back level. The haunches were comparatively full towards the hips but light downwards and altogether small in proportion to the fore-parts. Legs were of a moderate length with extremely fine and remarkably light bone throughout. The pelt was thin and the tail small. The wool was shorter than longwools in general but much longer than the middle wools. The ordinary length of the staple was 5 in. to 7 in. varying in fineness and weight. 'The carcase when fully fat takes on a remarkable form, much wider than it is deep and almost as broad as it is long. Full on the shoulder and widest on the ribs, narrowing with a regular curve towards the tail, approaching the form of the turtle more than any other animal.'

Culley explained that the variety of Lincolnshire first selected by Bakewell was 'with singular discernment and great attention' changed to that of a sheep unknown in any former period, and which surpassed all other breeds in their ability to fatten and the return given for the amount of food consumed. He described the distinct differences from other longwool breeds: 'The fine lively eyes, clean head, straight broad flat back, the barrel-like form of the body, fine small bones, thin pelt and inclination to early maturity. The mutton fine-grained and of superior flavour. Wool averaging 8 lb to a fleece and in length from 6 in. to 14 in. Wethers killed for best profit at 2 years when making between 20–30 lb a quarter.'

When this is compared to the 'Old Leicestershire' breed of sheep we can fully understand Bakewell's great achievement. Marshall described a ram of the 'true old Leics. sort' which was shown at Leicester ram show in 1784. 'This creature might be said to be in the lowest form of degeneracy. A naturalist would have found some difficulty in classing him and seeing him on a mountain might have deemed him a cross between a sheep and a goat.' The old breed is portrayed as a truly ugly animal, of large frame and heavy bone. The legs were long and thick, culminating in large splayed feet, the body being extremely sharp and angular was not even improved by good pasture and animals generally did not go for slaughter before three or four years of age.

Marshall thought that the new breed surpassed any other that he had seen, and spoke of their 'positive beauty'. It appears that the most distinguishing characteristic of the sheep was its fullness and weight in the forequarters. It was usual for this breed to possess a projection of fat on the ribs immediately behind the shoulder. This gained the technical term of *foreflank*. This will seem to us most strange when in today's world an improved sheep would be heavier in the legs and saddle and not in the shoulders and breast, but Bakewell was catering for the market of the second half of the 18th century when fat mutton was the diet of the poor man. Bakewell was thus providing for the increased masses of the poor working class, his main aim of improvement being to supply their needs. Fat mutton at this time could be purchased for the equivalent of 5d per lb as opposed to 8d per lb for bacon. When salted and pickled for some time the mutton took on a striking resemblance in taste to bacon.

Marshall had the opportunity to study two carcases side by side, one of a Dishley, the other a Norfolk sheep. The differences were striking, the bone of the Norfolk being almost twice that of the Dishley and the meat of the Dishley three times thicker than that

*Leicester wethers, the property of G. L. Foljambe of Osberton Hall, near Retford, Notts, for which the first prize of £20 and silver and gold medals were awarded at the Smithfield Club Cattle Show in December 1859.*

of the Norfolk. This was evidence enough for Marshall to say that the Dishley was of more value to the consumer, for 'while mankind eats flesh, he throws away bone.'

There were two reasons why the wethers (castrated males) were killed at two years of age: first, this was when the most profit was to be had, and second, if kept any longer they became too fat for the more refined palate.

The following measurements were recorded by Arthur Young at Dishley, on 17 March 1770:

I have this day measured Mr Bakewell's three year old ram, and find him as follows

|  | ft | inches |
|---|---|---|
| His girth | 5 | 10 |
| His height | 2 | 5 |
| His collar broad at ear tips | 1 | 4 |
| Broad over his shoulders | 1 | 11½ |
| Broad over his ribs | 1 | 10½ |
| Broad over his hips | 1 | 9½ |

This day measured a two year old barren ewe:

| | | |
|---|---|---|
| Height | 1 | 11 |
| Girth | 5 | 9 |

Breast from the ground, the breadth of four fingers.
N.B. – I would have measured her breast but for a fall of snow.

Marshall tells us that 'The degree of fatness to which the individuals of this breed are capable of being raised, will, I am afraid, appear incredible to those who have not had an opportunity of being convinced by their own observation.' He had seen two- to three-year-old wethers so fat they were hardly able to run 'and whose fat lay so much about the bone, it seemed ready to be shook from the ribs at the smallest agitation'. In 1786 he saw wethers barely a year old selling for 28 shillings a head as opposed to the common sheep which sold for 18 shillings each. In February 1785 Marshall was shown a forequarter of mutton by Mr Prinsep of Croxall which had 4 in. of fat on the ribs. In October 1783 James Bolton of Alnwick is on record that when his three-year-old wether of the Dishley breed was killed it measured

7⅛ in. of fat upon the ribs, and had a back like the fattest bacon. Another extraordinary point in this breed was that the rams and some of the females were termed as 'cracked in the back', that is, they had a channel running the length of the chine. Any animal showing this condition was said to be of the very best blood.

The Dishley was not only remarkable for its mutton being fat but also for its fine grain and excellent flavour. The grain in the meat of other breeds tended to be coarse and sponge-like.

Bakewell attracted a great many followers with his Dishley breed of sheep and numbered amongst them were many leading men of the Midland counties.

# CHAPTER THREE

# Ram Letting and the Dishley Society

From the inspection of these rules, it will be evident that the tendency of the first four was to preserve the purity of this new breed of sheep, and the peculiar excellencies of the sort. . . . The remaining nine rules have for their object evidently the establishment of as close a monopoly as could be effected among the members of the Society.

*(W. Youatt, 1837)*

Although Robert Bakewell is famous mainly for the fact that he bred a new type of sheep, he in effect devised a considerable number of new techniques of sheep management. These had two main effects: the better identification of sheep worth bringing into his breeding programme, and the faster growth of the sheep, subject to some deliberate management restraints, which were in that programme.

Although ram letting originated in Lincolnshire, it was Bakewell who took up the idea and popularised it. Every year, private shows were held by the principal breeders for the purpose of letting rams. An example of this can be seen at the Tate Gallery in London, in a painting by Thomas Weaver entitled 'Ram Letting at Dishley'.

By common consent of the top breeders, the ram letting shows would begin on 8th June and last until Michaelmas. During this period every ram breeder kept open house. Parties of breeders would travel from one show to another. These private exhibitions closed with a *public* show at Leicester on 10th October when mostly only inferior rams would be left.

The rams were brought to Leicester in waggons to be sold or let, with many coming from considerable distances. Leicester Ram Show had been a fixture from time immemorial, although before Bakewell's time it had been purely a means of selling rams. It was Bakewell who introduced letting to the Midlands with a ram which he let for 16 shillings in 1760. This single event was to lead to great wealth being brought to the Midland counties. Bakewell adopted the method of showing his rams separately so that they could not be judged one against another. This, to a good judge of sheep, did not matter, but by others it was greatly disliked as it gave no guide of comparison. Bakewell and his followers adopted the custom of letting their customers value the rams as they thought, and then bid a price. Rams in this way could be let to the highest bidder; it also allowed the owner to regulate the price to the customer without giving open offence.

There was great competition between breeders, and it was better for an owner to let his best ram for less money to a man with poor stock than to let him to a competitor with ewes nearly as good as his own, for by that method the competitor would soon overtake him. Also, if two good breeders formed a partnership to hire a superior ram, thus dispersing his blood widely, the price for letting would fit the number of partners who would gain by the use of him. No legal transaction ever took place at the letting of a ram, it was simply a gentleman's agreement. If no pregnancy resulted no money would be paid. If the ram died while away, almost regardless of the circumstances, the loss fell on the owner. The hirer could only use the ram on a stipulated number of ewes. If the hirer was merely a grazier he was not allowed to rear any ram lambs.

Ram letting was a most serious business and in 1783 Bakewell founded the Dishley Society whose aims were to preserve the purity of the Dishley breed of sheep, and also to protect and advance the interests of the breeders who, between them, had established a breed which was capable of improving other breeds by astonishing amounts. Much ill-will was unleashed against its principle men in the press for reportedly overcharging gullible young men of means for whom, at the time, agriculture was very much in vogue. But our improvers had invested much time, money and effort into raising the standards of the country's flocks.

They felt they had a just cause for recompense for their outlay. Realising that they would be the losers if they did not combine to protect their assets, by charging high prices they ensured the quality of their product was not only maintained but continually improved, for people would be very selective in choosing the best ewes to put to an expensive ram.

The Society was a great success. Prices, as bid by buyers and leasers of rams, rose sharply and so did the envy of those who did not belong to this elite band of men. Bakewell, being the founder, was singled out and held mostly responsible for alleged acts of misconduct. Houseman, writing in 1894, refuted the allegations. He suggested that men of such strong morals as Arthur Young and William Marshall, to name but two, would never have vouched for Bakewell if there had been one grain of truth in them. Bakewell was not a ready communicator to men who did not share his vision for improvement. It can well be imagined that he would give short shrift to the likes of jobbing journalists who in turn would fan the flames with allegations of mystery and secret practices.

In 1786, by letting 20 rams, Bakewell made 1,000 guineas. By 1789 he earned 1,200 guineas for letting three brothers and 2,000 guineas for seven other rams. It was estimated that the total amount made from ram letting in that season by Bakewell and six or seven other prominent Midland breeders was the incredible sum of £10,000.

It was rumoured at the time that these prices were totally false and that, although a high sum was paid out, a great proportion of it was handed back in what is termed 'luck money'. This belief was pointed out by Marshall as being totally false. Although the practice may have occurred in the early dawn of the procedures it had long since ceased. 'Mr Bakewell, being well known for his economy, certainly was not known to give more than five shillings on a high-priced transaction and for any below 50 guineas only half-a-crown.'

The high prices paid for the hire of rams was not given by the graziers, who wanted their produce for the meat market, but by *ram breeders* for the purpose of breeding ram lambs which were then let to the graziers. The highest prices were given by the top or principal breeders for the purpose of getting rams which were then let to inferior tupmen, as ram-getters, the progeny of which were then let to the graziers. The price a grazier gave on average for hiring a ram was 5 or 6 guineas. The improved Leicester ram produced for him a sheep which would fatten by two years instead of the usual three or four years and make 10–15 shillings more when sold.

Rams were brought into high condition for the shows, but as soon as a let had been agreed they would be put onto poor pasture to bring them back into working condition. Rams usually remained serviceable until the age of five years, at which point they would have become too fat for use and with that condition came a multitude of health problems. The rams would be sent out for the tupping season during the middle of September. They were transported in two-wheeled sprung carriages or hung in slings which could hold up to four at a time. In this way a distance of 20–30 miles a day could be completed, as many of them had great distances to travel to their final destination.

The Dishley Society's principal rules were:

1. No member shall hire or use a ram not belonging either to Mr Bakewell or to one of the members of the Society.
2. No member of the Society shall give his rams, at any season of the year, any other food than green vegetables, hay and straw.
3. No member shall let more than 30 rams in any one season.
4. No member shall let a ram for less than 10 guineas to any person, nor for less than 40 guineas to any person who lets rams.
5. No ram shall be let to serve the flocks of more than two persons.
6. No member shall let a ram to any one who lets or sells his rams at fairs or markets.
7. No member shall take in ewes to be served by more than one ram, at his own residence, in any one season, unless they belong to members of the Society, nor to be served by any ram he uses for his own flock, with the same exception.
8. Mr Bakewell engages not to let any ram for less than 50 guineas to any person residing within 100 miles of Dishley.
9. No member shall let a ram to any person residing within 30 miles of Leicester and, not being a member of the Society,

who shall have hired a ram of Mr Bakewell during the preceding season.

10. No member shall sell any ewes or rams of his own breed, to breed from, unless he sells his whole flock of sheep, except to members of the Society.

11. From 1st to the 8th of June the members shall not show their rams, except to one another. They shall begin their general show on the 8th of June, and continue to show their rams until the 8th of July; from that day until the 8th of September they shall not show them to anyone, but shall open their show again and continue it until the end of the season.

12. On the 8th and 9th of June, although the rams may be shown, no ram shall be let or engaged to be let, nor shall the price which will be required for him be mentioned by anyone.

13. Every member, refusing or neglecting to abide by the rules of the Society, or withdrawing himself from it, shall no longer be considered a member. From that time he shall not be permitted to hire any ram or share of a ram from any of its members, until readmitted into the Society at a general meeting.

The members of the first meeting were Wm Walker, J. V. Stone, Jno. Bennett, Jno. Manning, Jos. Robinson, Nath. Stubbins, Nich Buckley, R. Bakewell, F. White, Jno. Breedon, Saml. Knowles, President Mr T. Paget, Treasurer R. Honeybourne.

Prominent breeders who were later members of the Dishley Society included the Duke of Bedford, the Marquess of Buckingham, Lord Egrement, of Petworth, Sussex, Wm Coke (later Earl of Leicester) of Holkham, Norfolk, and Messrs Martin of Clifton, Nottingham, Weston of Brackley, Northants, Creek of Rousham, Oxfordshire, Prinsep of Croxall, Staffordshire, Collins of Darlington, Co. Durham, Culley of East Field, Fenton, Northumberland, and Sale of Wentbridge, Yorkshire.

Another introduction of Bakewell's was the use of teaser rams. Today, a teaser ram is a vasectomised male which is still capable of indicating when a ewe is in oestrus, but is incapable of fertilisation. When introduced to a batch of ewes, he stimulates them to begin cycling, after which he is removed and a ram proper replaces him.

Bakewell's teasers were rams of little value whose genitals were covered by a cloth to prevent any mating occurring. As soon as a ewe showed in season to the teaser, she was removed and put to one of the best rams, which was kept in a pen on his own. The ewe's head was placed in stocks for mating, to prevent fatiguing the ram. By this method a ram could cover many more females.

The normal method of putting the ram to the complete batch of ewes to be served was gradually replaced by Bakewell's system. By this means a ram was capable of serving twice the number of ewes compared with the previous method. Up to 120 ewes became usual and one ram was recorded as having served 140.

The rams were returned to their owner by the hirer at the beginning of December. The owners then set to with a will in order to have them ready for the next show season. In general the principal ram breeders kept flocks of 100–200 ewes while graziers would have 500–600 ewes.

No cost or labour was spared in the attentions lavished on the ewes at lambing by the principal breeders, as their offspring were of extreme value as potential rams for letting. The ewes were pushed to produce a good flush of milk to give the lambs the best possible start.

Cull ewes were sold by the graziers after four shear (that is, four annual crops of wool), but the ram breeders kept their best ewes until they could no longer breed. The principal breeders did not let such valuable assets off their property alive but slaughtered them at home, so that they could not be used for further breeding by their new owners who were not in the breeding circle (eventually the Dishley Society).

But Bakewell, being Bakewell, had discovered his own method of ensuring that ewes sold for a slaughter price were not used for breeding. At this time liver fluke was causing considerable problems for sheep farmers, but it had come to the attention of the ever-watchful Bakewell that, before the middle of May, sheep could be safely grazed on land that had been flooded, but that after that time the sheep became fluked.

Any sheep that were sold for slaughter were therefore grazed on pastures in the autumn which had been artificially flooded during the summer. Consequently, when he sold them he knew that they were certain to be suffering from the effects of 'rot' or liver fluke. This caused no loss of fitness but, on the contrary, caused the sheep in the early stages of the condition to fatten all the quicker. By these means Bakewell gained up to six weeks in the accumulation of condition in his own sheep over that of his neighbours' sheep and into the bargain he was assured that their fate was sealed.

As can be seen, Bakewell left no stone unturned in his quest for perfection. Every aspect of husbandry was covered. He was a great showman and his stock were also produced for exhibition to the very best of his, and his men's, abilities. It is reported that his sheep were kept as clean as racehorses, with his best animals even wearing body clothes.

## Objections to the Dishley Sheep

Mr Wright of Chesterfield wrote in 1830 that at one point Bakewell's sheep became too small, fine, light-woolled and effeminate, the result of constantly using light-boned, small rams. The great strides forward in mutton production came at no little cost, for milk production fell and, with the short bone of the legs, lambs found it difficult to suckle. When Bakewell realised that his breeding policy was having a detrimental effect on his flock, he made a judicious cross to a larger ram and thus amended the problem. The length of leg was increased again, making it easier for the nursing lamb and also making the walk to market less stressful for culls. Thus he left at his death two very different types of Leicester sheep.

In 1809 Pitt reported a remark made by Bakewell to a gentleman who was complaining 'That his mutton was so fat that he could not eat it'. 'Sir,' was the reply, 'I do not breed sheep for gentlemen but for the public.' Not many years after his death this answer would not have served him, for the public as well as the gentlemen gained a taste for leaner mutton.

John Lawrence, writing in 1805, was clearly no follower of the Leicester or Dishley sheep. He reveals that the first thing that sprang to mind on inspecting his last line-up of prize winners of this breed was 'the facility with which a certain form is converted into a living grease tub'. He also related the story of the night he dined out when a leg of prize mutton made up one of the dishes:

'The joint was 17 lb in weight, at my desire the fat which dripped in cooking was measured and it amounted to between 2 and 3 quarts, besides which the serving dish was a bog of loose, oily fat, huge deep flakes of it remained to garnish that which we called, by courtesy, lean, being itself also thoroughly interleaved and impregnated. It struck me forcibly, that an addition of a reasonable quantity of bone, and exchange of 7 or 8 lbs of fat for lean meat, would have contributed much to the actual value and good character of the joint. Little of it was eaten at our table, and I have reason to believe, not much more at the other tables.'

Lawrence researched the subject and found that by 1805 labourers usually rejected over-fat mutton if there was a choice, for from necessity they had to eat up all they bought, whereas the rich could admire, taste and throw away that which they did not require. He laid the charge that the Dishley sheep provided rich men's mutton. 'The late fashionable excess in fattening even pork and bacon has generally disgusted the labourers, in consequence, much wanton waste has ensued, and the dealers in such produce, now find difficulty in their disposal.'

## Bakewell's Experiments

As well as sheep of his own creation, Bakewell also kept other breeds at Dishley for use in comparison trials and also for crossing his own rams on to, to see if improvement could be made with the other breed. It is probably because visitors saw sheep of other breeds, and also Leicester crosses, that it was believed that many types made up Bakewell's recipe for success.

One visitor recalled seeing three sheep which were produced by one ewe but by different rams. One was by a Ryeland, one by a Spanish and one by a Dishley ram. The difference between them was said to be very great, with the offspring of the Dishley being far superior to the others. This was obviously an experiment to test the merits of various crosses.

Details are given in Arthur Young's *Annals*, Vol. VI, of his second visit to Dishley in 1785. 'I was witness at Dishley to a very interesting experiment on different breeds of sheep. He has a sheep house in which six rams were tied up and stalled on turnips:

one of his own breed, one Norfolk, one Teeswater, one Wiltshire, one from Ross in Herefordshire and one from Charnwood Forest. They were weighed alive when put to turnips, their food weighed to them, and weighed alive again at the end of the trial.'

The trial was conducted entirely by a young Russian, John Saphonkove, resident at Dishley at the time, to whom Mr Bakewell entrusted the work, as the trial was not on a scale to which he could attend himself. It was therefore conducted in a very fair manner. Young attended the sheep-weighing and vouched for the accuracy of the figures, although he gives only the final weights for the sheep:

|  | Weight of the sheep | Turnips from 19 March to 2 April 1786 |
| --- | --- | --- |
| Durham | 290 lb | 498 lb |
| Wiltshire | 173 | 313 |
| Norfolk | 162 | 298 |
| Dishley | 158 | 174 |
| Charnwood Forest | 131 | 304 |
| Herefordshire | 115 | 202 |

Modern trialists would, of course, heavily criticise the figures on a number of grounds. There was only one sheep of each breed; they had been chosen by Bakewell and probably not all were representative of the best of their breed; no increases in liveweight gains were given; and, most important of all, no carcase weights were attempted. They would nevertheless provide 'impressions' of the relative performance of the different breeds. Conclusions would doubtless be drawn.

Arthur Young related the following information in Vol. VII of his *Annals*, in 1786:

Mr Wyn Baker, who was employed by the Dublin Society of Agriculture to make experiments, says it would require about 20 weeks to fat a sheep completely on turnips and that he would consume, during that time, one fourth of his mutton weight a day, that is, the weight of his four quarters when killed (which is reckoned about half his liveweight just before killing). Therefore, sheep, whose mutton weight would be 80 lb would consume 20 lb of turnips a day, or 140 lb, or 10 stone a week; and as

160 stone is a ton weight, a ton of turnips would maintain 16 such sheep a week.

Mr Wyn Baker remarks that the sheep to be fatted will not require above a quarter of their mutton weight a day, yet oxen will require half their beef weight per day, although beef and mutton, at market, sell at nearly the same price.

These figures from Mr Wyn Baker, allowing a quarter of the mutton weight of the sheep per day in turnips to fatten them, seem to confirm the experiment made at Bakewell's farm on six stalled rams which consumed about one-eighth of their liveweight a day. That was with the exception of Bakewell's own Dishley breed, which did not consume above one-twelfth of his liveweight per day.

*This portrait of Valentine Barford was presented to him by his friends as a token of respect for his upright conduct and his perseverance and ability in keeping up the true character and form of the pure-bred Bakewell Leicester sheep in 1850.*

Reference is made in 1828 by Mr Valentine Barford that, according to Bakewell's friend and fellow-member of the Dishley Society, Richard Astley of Odstone, a black ram had been used at Dishley in the mid-1780s on the New Leicester flock. Barford was himself a New Leicester breeder (of Foscote, Northants), whose flock was directly descended from Bakewell's. In a letter to the Rev. Henry Berry, he records that no flock of New Leicesters had produced more black rams than his, although he retained none for breeding. Barford's flock had been carefully recorded from its beginning in a private pedigree register. It was closely interbred with the flock of Joseph Robinson, a founder member of the Dishley Society, who, in turn, had closely interbred his own flock from Bakewell's. It would appear that Black Leicester longwools have continuously cropped up through the ages, although up until the recent introduction of their own register, they were ineligible for registration.

The story of the black ram is related as a point of interest but not as conclusive evidence that such an animal was indeed used. It may have been that Astley, having seen a black ram at Dishley, assumed that it was being made use of in the New Leicester flock. Astley also fell foul of the Dishley Society rules, incurring heavy fines, so this may have been his way of getting back at Bakewell.

An incident revealing Bakewell's sense of humour, and also explaining the presence of two black-faced rams at Dishley, is related by the Rev. Henry Berry. Bakewell, with the assistance of the shepherd at Holkham in Norfolk (on the famous estate of Coke, later Lord Leicester) secretly removed two Norfolk rams from Coke's flock during his absence. Coke regularly exchanged visits with Bakewell and, on his next trip to Dishley, he was treated to the usual parade of magnificent Dishley rams. But then came a sight for which he was totally unprepared – his own formidable-looking Norfolk rams were led past, each wearing a neck collar, and with thick spiral horns, black feet and legs and long bodies. 'At a given signal, away they bolted at top speed, each clearing the hurdles in high style and then, returning, accomplished the same feat.' No one enjoyed a practical joke more than Berry's informant – Mr Coke himself.

# CHAPTER FOUR

# Old Lincoln v. New Leicester

I have not used any Lincolnshire Rams for 20 years past –
why have you at different times from the year 1773 to
1786, hired from this county?

*(Robert Bakewell, 1788)*

It has been mentioned before that the Dishley or New Leicester
sheep were used to improve many other breeds. Among them
was the breed to which they are reputed to owe their derivation,
the Old Lincolnshire. This breed was crossed so extensively with
the New Leicester that they were eventually to disappear. For
over a quarter of a century great ill-feeling was generated between
the purist breeders of Lincolns and the new improvers.

In 1788, Bakewell fell out most bitterly with Mr Charles
Chaplin, a breeder of the Old Lincoln. Chaplin strongly held that,
in his opinion, the Old Lincoln was a far better animal than the
new improved type, which had been produced by the introduction of New Leicester blood.

Arthur Young's *Annals of Agriculture*, Vol. 10, gives us access to
the angry exchanges between these two men. A proposal had
been made in 1788 to hold a ram show at Partney, one of the
ancient Lincolnshire sheep fairs, so that the Old Lincoln could be
compared with the 'New Improved Lincoln'. Bakewell declined
to allow his sheep to be viewed before the event, when they
would be in top show condition. But, being in his rival's neighbourhood, he took advantage of Chaplin's absence to have a sneak
preview of the competition, in their natural condition. Chaplin
greatly resented this act and wrote Bakewell the following letter:

The extraordinary art made use of in the exhibition of your stock at Dishley points out, in the strongest possible manner, the impropriety of showing it in a disorderly state and, after my refusal on the 21st to let you see my sheep before they were collected and sorted at home, I did not expect to hear of you meanly sneaking into my pastures at Wrangle on the 24th with two other people, driving my sheep into a fold and examining them. Such unwarrantable conduct can only be accounted for by your anxiety about the show of rams at Partney, near Spilsby, on the 18th September, which was proposed for the purpose of making the comparison between those bred from your sheep and the original breed of the County. The small sheep that have no cross of the Durham kind which you have had the address to impose upon the world, without size, without length and without wool, I have always felt to be unprofitable animals. But that I may not be too tenacious of my own opinion, I hope you will produce them at Partney on 18th September to meet the Lincoln sheep, where they will be met by better judges than ourselves to decide on their merits.

Bakewell replied:

On my return home on Tues last, I saw your letter addressed to me for the 26th Aug. in the Leicester paper of the 6th of Sept, in which you are pleased to notice the extraordinary art made use of the exhibition of stock at Dishley, which you have seen on several occasions. Surely you cannot say you have observed any unfair practices, or that you were ever denied access to anything that was not out on loan, because it was not sorted or in a disorderly state? At Horncastle on Thurs 21st Aug, I asked you if I might see your rams near Saltfleet. You did not say I should not, but that they were not sorted, and that when they were you would be glad to see me at Tathwell. I did not go to Saltfleet but into the marshes near Skegness and, from there, on Saturday afternoon, to Wrangle. The next day I went to Freeston where I met two graziers whom I did not know. They proposed to go to Skegness on Monday and asked me if I thought they could see your rams. I told them that I was informed on my way to, and at, Wrangle, that they might. We set off together and called at the inn at Wrangle, which I came from the day before, and there passed what you are pleased to term my 'meanly sneaking into your pastures on the 24th'. We asked a young man there if you had any rams there, he told us you had. 'Where are they?' 'In the close next the house.' 'May we see them?' 'Yes.' 'Who would show them?' 'I will', from which we supposed he often showed them to others. We went to the close and assisted in driving 14 rams into the pen. The age or breed of them I do not know. From there we went to your shepherd, a further 1½ miles, and asked if we could see them. He refused, saying he had received orders in a letter from you, to show them to no one. He was then asked if he had shown them before. He had. 'When did he receive the order not to show them?' 'On Saturday night last.' Had we know this before, we should not have been guilty of what you term 'such unwarrantable conduct'. I have long made it a rule not to find fault with another person's stock. Why should you be so severe on mine? And I now take the liberty of asking you to explain what you mean by 'sheep without size, without length, and without wool', which you say I have had the address to impose upon the world; and of informing you that I am fully persuaded that there are ten rams without a cross of the Durham, or any other kind, let for 1,000 gns more this season than the same number of the 'True Old Lincolnshire breed of the long staple', some of these at the highest prices, into the counties of Lincoln and Nottingham, and to breeders, many of whom have used the Dishley sort of sheep for upwards of 20 years, and who have agreed for some, and offer higher prices for others, for future seasons, than they have yet given, and may surely be supposed capable of knowing the value of what 'you have always held to be unprofitable animals'. Did they not find their interest in so doing, would they persevere? The address must be extraordinary, indeed, that could impose upon them against their interest and so long experience.

Give me leave to ask, Sir, had you such sheep, would you at this time of the year incur the expense and run the hazard of sending them 80 miles from home, to gratify the curiosity of breeders in this neighbourhood? If you are still desirous of a public exhibition, please to say if you would choose to send on the 5th July next, to Lincoln and to Leicester (as there is a fair at both places on that day) 2 rams of the 'true Lincolnshire breed of the long staple' to each place, to be shown against the same number of the Dishley sort, weighed alive, killed, and an exact amount given of the carcasses and the offals, for the information of the public.

I am, Sir, your humble servant.

Robert Bakewell Sept 12, 1788.

Bakewell's gasping indignation at Chaplin's remarks is quite tangible. His anger is conveyed in his lengthy sentences, even to the reader after all these years.

Chaplin had not finished. From Tathwell on 19 September 1788 he wrote:

TO THE GENTLEMEN who attended Partney Fair on the 18th of this month:

GENTLEMEN,
It is unnecessary for me to say anything about the show of sheep yesterday, but as Mr Bakewell and myself, after having attempted in your presence to agree upon an experiment, likely to give to the public a fair insight into the comparative merit of our respective breeds of sheep, parted yesterday, under an agreement to meet this morning at Sir Joseph Banks's and there finally to settle the business. It is proper that I should give you an account of the result of that meeting.

Mr Coke of Norfolk, Sir Joseph Banks, and several gentlemen whom Mr Bakewell had brought with him, were present, when after some previous conversation, I made him the following offer, as a fair modification of the proposal made by him to me in the General Evening Post of Tuesday the 16th instant.

OFFER

To show at Midsummer next, two rams of my own breed, and my own property, with their wool on. To have them shorn, and then killed, and to have their fleeces, mutton, tallow, and offal weighed separately, on condition that I should name the sheep now – and that Mr Bakewell would also now name two rams of his own breed, and his own property, with which he would meet mine, and which he would subject to the same experiment at the same time.

To this proposal Mr Bakewell declined giving any answer, but he seemed inclined to close with a similar one, provided he should be allowed to produce such rams, as between now and Midsummer next, he might be able to procure, and he said, that I had the same opportunity as he had, to search all England for the best that could be got.

In which, knowing that your enquiries chiefly pointed at a comparison between the Lincolnshire and Leicestershire breeds, and unwilling to show against all England, as in that case Rams of my own sort might be brought in competition with me, I positively refused my acquiescence, a refusal, Gentlemen, I hope you will think me justified in.

And now I take leave to say that, as on several occasions in which I have had an opportunity of observing Mr Bakewell's conduct, it has not, in my opinion, been bounded by that rigid line of propriety with which I have ever earnestly endeavoured to circumscribe my own, I think myself at liberty to decline all further controversy with him, and unless he, or some of his people, are again caught sneaking into my pastures, to examine my unsorted stock, or doing some other thing of similar impropriety, he may rest secure from being again either publicly addressed, or answered by.

Your most obedient servant

CHARLES CHAPLIN.

P.S. If anyone wishes to be satisfied of the comparative merit of the Lincolnshire and Leicestershire wool, let him enquire at Leeds and Wakefield, and at Smithfield he may learn from which county the best sheep for mutton are sent.

Bakewell eventually saw this letter of Chaplin's, as was doubtless intended, and he replied:

To CHARLES CHAPLIN Esq.

Sir,

Your letter of the 19th Sept., addressed to the gentlemen who attended at Partney, I should have noticed sooner, but that I waited for some information relative to what Rams you have had from this county, a business you always appeared to transact in the most private manner.

On the 25th of August, it is true, I went into a piece of rich grazing land, next to the public house in the town of Wrangle, and there saw fourteen Rams, which I understood had been shown before to anyone who asked to see them, therefore, I could not consider them as unsorted or in a disorderly state. This did not arise, as you are pleased to state it, from any anxiety of mine about the Show of Rams at Partney, with which I never intended to have any concern, though probably it might cause your anger, lest I might have discovered how those were bred, which were intended for that exhibition.

For this *heinous offence*, in your first letter, you severely condemn my sheep. In your second, hint at my character, and compliment your own. Your manner of noticing my conduct and stock, I consider as a very fortunate circumstance, as it gives me an opportunity of making some remarks on yours, for which I should otherwise have mounted an apology. I shall take the liberty of asking you the following questions, to which, when I have your answers, I will lay before you and a candid public, the conditions on which I will meet you at *Lincoln, Leicester*, and as many other county towns as you please. I conceive that you and I showing two rams each, without saying how they were bred, and which on this account might not do any business this season, and might be highly fed nine months for the showing at *Lincoln* only, can throw but little light on this important subject, and be of small consequence towards ascertaining the merits of the true old Lincolnshire, and new Leicestershire sort of sheep.

Why do you give your Rams anything but grass, hay or turnips in winter, or anything but grass in summer? Why do you refuse to show them, except at particular times? Mine that are not engaged, you may see any day in the year, Sundays, and the first seven days in June, excepted. When may I be favoured with a sight of yours?

Why, at a time when shearlings are let at such high prices, and lambs are letting at still higher, for the next season, do you show or let so few of that age?

Why, when Rams are let so high, and sixty Ewes descended from this stock were sold by auction the 14th of Sept., 1787, at more than 5 gns. each, and some of them into the county of Lincoln, and many cull Ewes have since been sold at much more, do so many of yours of both sorts go to market?

Why are they not rather bought to breed from, when they may be had at butchers' price?

Why do so many of the Lincolnshire breeders, who will give the best prices, go into other counties for their Rams?

Why do you, who have formerly sent so many Rams into this county, now send so few — if any?

Can you inform me of any of the Leicestershire Breeders, who will show Rams at this time, and say they are of your kind?

Since the time when 5 of your Rams were advertised to serve Ewes, in as many different places, at half-a-crown each — a Ram, bred in your county, son of a Leicestershire Ram, has been advertised in your neighbourhood, to serve Ewes at a guinea each! Have the prices of yours advanced in the same proportion?

I have not used any Lincolnshire Rams for 20 years past – why have you at different times from the year 1773 to 1786, hired from this county?

Why did you in the year 1783, *buy four*, besides what you hired? If you had not found an advantage in this, who could have address enough to impose such upon you, and induce you to continue the practice for so many years? If such as you have had from this county have improved the good old Lincolnshire Sheep, some think you had not a cross before it was wanted, and that some of the Rams you showed at Partney, were descended from the Leicestershire kind – Can you prove the contrary?

Can anyone after this be at a loss to know what the Leicestershire Breeders think of Lincolnshire sheep, and *you*, of those which *you say*, you 'have always held to be unprofitable animals'. If you have not more of this sort, do not take more pains in handling those you choose, and pay a little more attention to the *carcass* than you have hitherto done. Beware, that (notwithstanding all the art you can make use of, *feeding*, in *shearing* and *dressing*) – some of your spirited and unprejudiced neighbours, do not cause you to go out of the RAM BUSINESS – *in the same manner as you have represented me going into your pastures* at WRANGLE.

I am, Sir, your humble servant
ROBERT BAKEWELL
Dishley, Nov 19, 1788.

# CHAPTER FIVE

# Bakewell's Legacy

Every branch of the agricultural art was more or less
indebted to him, his fortunate genius and his original mind.

The experiments which Bakewell carried out with his sheep
are legion, but it is not my purpose to retell them all here.
This is really the Longhorn story and so we must pass lightly
over many of those matters which Bakewell touched with his
magician's wand. But let it be said that he tested his capabilities on
many subjects, including the production of a superior 'Black
Leicestershire Carthorse'. This began with a number of West
Friesland mares which he purchased while touring Holland and
part of Flanders in the company of Mr G. Salisbury, and which he
felt excelled in the points he thought defective in his own stock.
'With great labour, expense and judgement he produced a breed
of capital horses,' and he had the honour of exhibiting one to
George III in 1785.

Bakewell's strain was lighter-legged and flatter-boned than the
horses which came later, but of great strength, especially in the
forequarters, with erect heads and fine crests. He was famed as the
best breeder of horses during his lifetime. Even his mares were
used in work teams but they were treated as gently as a man would
treat his wife, and the use of the whip was entirely prohibited at
Dishley.

From William Pitt comes this 1809 comment on Bakewell's pigs,
thought to be of Berkshire origin. 'The improvement of hogs in
Leicestershire has been attended to with the same care and success,
as other livestock. At Dishley, some years back, a fine-boned sort,

of small dimensions, had been carried to great perfection. I have seen there, a hog of small size, when lean, but which fatted to 20 score weight, or more. His length, height and thickness being nearly equal, his belly touching the ground, the legs being enveloped in fat, the whole appearing a mass of solid flesh. I measured a hog killed there, 13½ inches through the chine.'

John Monk noted in 1794: 'In one particular sty are appliances for measuring and weighing the food of hogs, and also for noting down the results, which are done by a servant with a piece of chalk kept there for the purpose, until they can be entered in the record book. This helped to prevent mistakes and to give conclusive evidence for the experiments.'

Bakewell even turned his gaze to the humble cabbage, for which he became nearly as famous as for his sheep. The cabbage he propagated was a large stock-feed variety of high nutritional value and hardiness. Great care was taken in raising the seed to keep it pure and prevent any cross-fertilisation by other brassicas. For this reason it was grown on plots surrounded by corn. It was chiefly fed to sheep, although occasionally used for other stock.

Marshall declared Bakewell to be the 'greatest cabbage grower' he had ever seen.

He also had revolutionary ideas on hedge planting, road building and the production of fertiliser and was credited with being the first to plough with only two horses abreast instead of the more usual four in tandem. He was a great supporter of new machinery inventions, using, amongst other things, the Rotherham plough and Cooke's improved drill, a variation by the Rev. Cooke on the principle established by Jethro Tull.

He was also fortunate in having machinery makers in his local village, Hathern. Messrs Hanford and Co. were no doubt able to turn his ideas into reality. It was certainly from them that he obtained a hopper attachment for his plough, by means of which he was able to sow beans at the same time as ploughing – now quite a common practice.

In his report on Leicestershire Agriculture to the first Board of Agriculture in 1794, John Monk noted that there was a blacksmith's shop at Dishley where two men were employed in making tools and implements for the farm, and in repairing those that were broken. This clearly gave Bakewell the capacity to develop many of his practical ideas ranging from new designs for gates to innovations for his irrigation system. The gardens are reported to have been 'sometimes irrigated', even though they were described as being of a 'swampy nature', not far from the River Soar.

The great agricultural improvers of the period, like Bakewell, had to finance their experiments out of their own pockets, as there was no Board (or Ministry) of Agriculture funded by the state to carry out such research. Nor was the Board, eventually founded in 1793, in a position to fund research. Both Bakewell and William Marshall were, though, strong advocates of such an institution, as was Arthur Young, who became its first secretary.

When we learn, then, that in November 1776 Bakewell was declared bankrupt, it is perhaps not altogether surprising. The causes of his plight were cumulative, with the balance being finally tipped by bad debtors owing money for the hiring of sires. His position could not have been helped by the lavish hospitality to be had at Dishley, which was said to be in the same grand style as in the homes of the landed gentry when they entertained. It must also be allowed that this was a most unfortunate period for making money by the cultivation of the land. The disastrous war with America was said to have considerably reduced the price of produce. Wool, which constituted a proportion of Bakewell's income, greatly fell in price, selling for as little as nine shillings per tod (28 lb). And the personal cost which he shouldered in order to conduct his many and varied experiments was no small undertaking.

The day was saved by his many friends and acquaintances who felt they could not, and should not, stand idly by and witness the fall of a man to whom so much was owed by his contemporaries. A subscription list for voluntary contributions was opened and the list of subscribers reads like a *Who's Who* of the day. The Duke of Rutland himself gave 200 guineas.

Even at the time of his bankruptcy, Bakewell kept up his high position, for when his stock was valued (the unexpired term of his lease being included in the valuation), there was a balance in his favour of from £1,500 to £2,000. From documents that may be considered of the highest authority – the valuations that were placed in the hands of the trustees at that time – the following extract shows the prices at which a portion of his sheep were estimated:

|              |                   | £   | s  |
|--------------|-------------------|-----|----|
| Willow piece | 26 ewes and lambs | 81  | 18 |
| Top piece    | 19 ewes and lambs | 99  | 15 |
| Balk piece   | 6 shear hog rams  | 42  | 10 |
| Marl piece   | 6 ewes and lambs  | 31  | 10 |
| Thorpe close | 26 theaves        | 109 | 4  |
| Mill leys    | 10 shear hog rams | 200 | 0  |
| Mill close   | 10 shear hog rams | 260 | 0  |
| Cow close    | 3 rams            | 50  | 0  |
| ditto        | 3 rams            | 300 | 0  |

Ironically, after being made secure by his friends and followers, he was repaid the money, the lack of which had forced him into difficulty in the first place. So neither his herd nor his flock was ever dispersed in his lifetime and he was quickly able to take up his mantle once more and carry on with the task for which the nation should evermore be grateful.

## Leicestershire Agricultural Society

The Leicestershire Agricultural Society was formed in 1788, with Bakewell as one of the subscribers. The Dishley Society, formed in 1783, although of a rather more exclusive nature, was therefore obviously the forerunner of the county society. Amazingly, and by great good fortune, the Leicestershire Society will be holding its 154th show on Dishley Grange itself in the very year of the bicentenary of Bakewell's death, 1995. A strong contingent of Longhorn cattle is expected to be present at the show.

One wonders what the Great Man himself would think of the vast strides in all sectors of agriculture which have been taken since he himself set the wheels in motion, with such vision and industry, so many years ago.

Arthur Young felt he could not conclude his observations of Bakewell's many undertakings 'without expressing the satisfaction I felt at viewing them. Nowhere have I seen works that do their author greater honour. They are not the effect of a rich landlord's attempts to be a good farmer on his own land but the truly meritous endeavours of a tenant performing great and expensive works on the property of another. Let me exhort the farmers of this kingdom in general to take Mr Bakewell as a pattern in many points of great importance. They will find only good can come of it and the kingdom in general will be benefited not a little.'

Although no memorial has ever been raised to the memory of the man whose achievements must stand alongside those of Jethro Tull, Charles Townshend and Coke of Norfolk, there can be no more fitting tribute than that which we see paraded before us at our agricultural shows today. They corroborate the achievements of the dedicated stockbreeders who have followed Bakewell down the ages and have given our country the reputation of being the stockyard of the world.

The following is an extract from the valuation of Dishley, taken in 1795, the year that the family's 99-year lease ran out and Robert Bakewell died:

| | | | | | |
|---|---|---|---|---|---|
| Mill Close | – one red cow and cow calf | – £35 | 0s | 0d |
| | – one cow and bull calf | – 50 | 0 | 0 |
| | – one cow and cow calf | – 40 | 0 | 0 |
| | – one two-year bull | – 70 | 0 | 0 |
| Land Piece | – one red cow and calf | – 40 | 0 | 0 |
| | – one cow and calf | – 60 | 0 | 0 |
| Brook Piece | – one cow and calf | – 35 | 0 | 0 |
| | – one cow and calf | – 30 | 0 | 0 |
| | – one cow | – 30 | 0 | 0 |
| | – one cow and cow calf | – 30 | 0 | 0 |
| Cows Close | – one bull | – 20 | 0 | 0 |
| Barn | – four bulls | – 105 | 0 | 0 |
| | – three cows | – 150 | 0 | 0 |
| | – three cows | – 60 | 0 | 0 |

After Robert Bakewell's death, the herd passed intact to his nephew, Robert Honeybourne, at valuation figures of between 20 and 70 guineas. Honeybourne lived and farmed at Dishley for a further 20 years, until his death, but sadly never measured up to his great predecessor. In his hands the great race of Dishley Longhorns was to wither and die, so that within a short period of Bakewell's death, there could scarcely be found a dozen true beasts of the kind within a 12-mile radius of Dishley itself. In 1844

Youatt likened the disappearance to that of 'some strange convulsion of nature, or some murderous pestilence' that had 'suddenly swept away all of this wonderful breed'.

During Honeybourne's time, Dishley lost all its importance and it quietly slipped back into the shadows, holding only a tenuous grip on the memory of those who quickly forgot this once venerated corner of the Leicestershire sod.

Bakewell's last few years were beset by health worries which he is said to have borne 'stoically'. He had always had a tendency to stoutness and, nearing the end of his days, 16 stone on the frame of a 5 ft 9 in. man can hardly have helped.

The year before his death he was again made president of the Dishley Society but, due to ill-health, had to stand down mid-term and hand over to his friend and compatriot, Thomas Paget of Ibstock, Leicestershire. Even when he was only 61, in 1787, it is to be seen in a letter he wrote to George Culley, that he felt time would not be left to him to carry out his life's work. He urged Culley, and all others of a like mind to his, to pursue his methods with 'unremitting zeal' as far as they possibly could. He reminded them always to have an eye for a superior way of thinking, should it emerge.

On 1 October 1795, at the age of 69, Robert Bakewell passed from this world to a better. His many obituaries are a great tribute to the man who was so obviously appreciated by many in his own lifetime. He provided the foundation and the inspiration for the great men who were to follow him.

Although in his lifetime he had a great aversion to selling his prize specimens, he developed an extensive letting business, with rams letting for as much as 1,000 guineas a season. He had always sought quality rather than size in an animal and founded a trend for small bone which was, after his death, taken to such an extreme that it can be cited as one of the main reasons for destroying the popularity of the Longhorn breed. J. Neville Fitt quite rightly stated: 'Moons wane, and races wither to the tomb.' The time of Bakewell and his contemporaries had finally ended.

Many of the men who followed in his wake lacked the skill of the master, and again in the words of J. Neville Fitt in 1876: 'Not content to leave well alone, in trying to gild refined gold, (they) overshot their mark, and produced misshapen animals, delicate in constitution and, worse than all, uncertain breeders.' They did not understand the principles of breeding as Bakewell and his contemporaries had and, ignoring qualities for which the Longhorn had been renowned, in their scramble to produce finer and finer bone, they sacrificed both size and constitution. The male of any species ought always to possess rough masculine properties but this most necessary qualification was neglected by the later breeders who strove only for long patchy rumps and hips, which had become the height of fashion, depth of rib and largeness of chest being considered of no or very little importance.

Towards the end of Bakewell's life, however, the great estimation in which the Longhorn was held can be judged by the following results of two sales held in September and November 1793. They were both conducted by a Mr Boot, the first for Nathaniel Pearce, to sell his Longhorn cattle and New Leicester sheep, the second for C. Cartwright to disperse his Lincolnshire sheep and Shorthorn cattle.

| | Mr Pearce | | | Mr Cartwright | | | Difference | | |
|---|---|---|---|---|---|---|---|---|---|
| | £ | s | d | £ | s | d | £ | s | d |
| Best score of ewes | 116 | 19 | 0 | 27 | 0 | 0 | 89 | 19 | 0 |
| Best score of wethers | 50 | 11 | 6 | 29 | 0 | 0 | 21 | 11 | 6 |
| 1 × bull   4 × cows | 331 | 5 | 6 | 38 | 15 | 0 | 292 | 10 | 6 |
| 3 × yearling heifers | 63 | 0 | 0 | 8 | 8 | 0 | 54 | 12 | 0 |
| TOTAL | 561 | 16 | 0 | 103 | 3 | 0 | 458 | 13 | 0 |

## Bakewell the Teacher

In Bakewell's time agricultural students were sent on to a farm to learn their trade, the cost varying with the ability of the tutor and the treatment the pupil expected to receive. The usual term was four years, and the cost ranged from £40 to £200.

Bakewell's first pupil was George Culley of Fenton, Northumberland, born in 1730 and destined to become one of his most fervent admirers and friends. He became famous for his flock of New Leicester sheep and for his chosen cattle breed, the Shorthorn, to which he applied his teacher's breeding principles. He was the author of *Observations on Livestock* (1786), probably

*Robert and Charles Colling (from an engraving by T. Thompson after the painting by T. Weaver).*

the first book ever written specifically on farm animals. This was a project about which Bakewell was most enthusiastic and encouraging.

Culley was a family friend of the Collings of Ketton, near Darlington, and was instrumental in arranging for the family's eldest son, Charles (who at that time was working for his father on the farm) to go, at the age of 31, as a pupil to Dishley. Charles, born in 1751, closely studied Bakewell's breeding system and was later joined by his brother, Robert. On returning home, the two of them applied their new-found knowledge to the popular breed in their area, the Shorthorn, and eventually eclipsed the deeds of their master. In their hands lay the doom of the Longhorn.

The foundation on which the Shorthorn empire was to be built was a bull called Hubback, which had caught the eye of Charles one Sunday as he made his way to church. The animal was quickly purchased but it actually did very little for the Collings, as he was sold on when his daughters entered the herd. It was to be some time before the Bakewell teachings were to sink in. In fact, it was to take an accidental mating, very much on the inbred line, with the result highly superior to the usual outcross, before the words of Bakewell began to hit home. Colling doubted no longer and from that point on his herd was as closely inbred as Bakewell's or Fowler's had been.

One of his earliest achievements was breeding the famous Ketton Ox, an animal regarded as faultless. It was by Favourite out of a common black and white cow bought at Durham Fair. Colling kept the beast for exhibition only, until, at the age of four years and weighing 3,024 lb (27 cwt or 1,371 kg), he was sold to Mr Bulmer of Harmby, North Yorkshire, in February 1801, for £140. The animal was sold again after six weeks to Mr John Day for £250 who, after changing its name to the Durham Ox, exhibited him all over the country at fairs and shows, causing tremendous excitement. Day received several large offers for him, but refused because the animal had become a pet of the family. The Durham Ox was finally slaughtered at Oxford in February 1807, after dislocating a hip.

It was to be to this animal that the writer, the Druid (H. H. Dixon), attributed the fall of the Longhorn race.

PART TWO

# The Story of the Longhorn

Oxley Bulloch

Mr Huskison Owner — 3 Years old 1795

# CHAPTER SIX

# Longhorns Before Bakewell

Where did he come from, this singularly picturesque beast
with the carriage of a lion and the temper of a dove – the
one breed in which, perhaps, the feeder, the butcher and
the artist may equally delight?

*(J. Neville Fitt, 1876)*

From the very earliest records of British agriculture there has
been a race of cattle set apart from most other breeds by
the great length of their horns. In the original types the horns
normally projected nearly horizontally on either side of the head.
But, as the cattle were improved, the horns assumed other directions, mostly in the shape known as bonnet or wheel horns.

Longhorns became predominant in medieval times over a large
area of the Midland counties and northern England. It is claimed
that, like its successor, the Shorthorn, the Longhorn first came
from Yorkshire, but from the more western part where the district
of Craven was said to be the cradle of the race. But the breed was
also very widely spread at an early date in our history throughout
what were known as 'the grazing districts' of the Midlands. It is
perhaps more feasible to assume that Craven was an area where,
for some reason, rather fine Longhorns were bred and, because of
their good qualities, they were introduced to other districts to
improve local stock, rather than being the one area from which
the whole of the Longhorn race first sprang.

J. Neville Fitt reported in 1876 that breeders had written letters
to him about their experiences with Longhorns. One Staffordshire
farmer spoke of the cattle being in his family for 280 years, thus

putting them there 180 years prior to Bakewell's era.

We learn that there were regional variations in the breed. The Lancashire, Westmorland, Cheshire, Derbyshire, Leicestershire, Nottinghamshire, Staffordshire, Oxfordshire and Wiltshire were all essentially Longhorn but each assumed a peculiarity of form which characterised it as belonging to a certain district and making it of value there.

Wherever they may originally have come from, the history of the Longhorn can only be traced with any accuracy from the northern part of Leicestershire and the neighbouring part of Derbyshire. J. Neville Fitt wrote that: 'He seems to have first been brought to perfection on the borders of the Charnwood Forest which, at the time these cattle first came into notoriety, was probably as wild and uncultivated as any spot to be found in England. Right well do the picturesque cattle match with its sylvan beauty.'

Could it be that the early pioneers of agricultural improvement were not only influenced by the breed's abilities to produce excellent beef and cheese, but were also susceptible to the beauty of these animals? It seems an extraordinary coincidence that perhaps the only breed of cattle which would stand out well against such a rugged landscape should have found its home in such an area.

## The Early Improvers

The earliest name to be encountered in connection with improvements in the Longhorn breed is that of Sir Thomas Gresley, of Drakelow House, Burton-upon-Trent, 'who took such delight in keeping a dairy of cows similar in colour and shape', in the early 1700s. At this time almost everyone who wished to improve their stock had resorted to using the bloodlines of Sir Thomas, and in general any Longhorn of note coming thereafter can be traced back to his herd.

A blacksmith and farrier by the name of Welby, living at Linton, near Sir Thomas, also goes on record as being a great improver of the breed. His stock were of the Drakelow line, and with great determination and willpower he built up a very valuable herd of cows. Unfortunately a disease, which at the time was totally incurable, wiped out most of them, nearly ruining Welby and putting a stop to any further hopes he had of cattle breeding.

John Webster of Canley, near Coventry, Warwickshire, next comes on the scene. The family had its origins as landowners in the Trent valley, and so were also neighbours of Sir Thomas Gresley. The Websters purchased six red Longhorn cows from Sir Thomas in 1710, and when John Webster moved to Canley after the death of his father in 1727, the Longhorns went too.

Webster bred the first historically famous bull of the breed regarded as the 'father of the race of improved Longhorns'. As a yearling he was considered so unpromising that he was sold on to a Mr Bloxedge. He turned out to be a very good stock-getter and Webster bought him back and used him for several seasons. Bloxedge, as he was called, was then sold on to a Mr Harrison of Deakenedge in Warwickshire, and later to Mr Flavell of Hogshill, Birmingham, where he finished his life.

Two eminent breeders of the day gave the following opinions of John Webster's cattle: 'That Mr Webster had the best stock of beace [beasts] that ever were, or (he believed) ever would be bred in the kingdom' and 'That in beauty or utility of form Longhorns

*Woodbine, the property of S. Burbery of Wroxhall, Warwicks, winner of first prize and silver medal at Bingley Hall in 1855.*

have improved little since Mr Webster's day, except in flesh, the more valuable quality, they have been improved.' This was great praise and was recorded as evidence of the superb quality of Webster's breed. A neighbour and good friend of Webster's, Mr Palfrey, in recalling the details of Webster's herd to agricultural writer William Marshall, said that, 'With regard to colour Webster favoured his six original red cows, but was much in favour of the brindled finch back and the pied.' The original six red cows were of a whole colour according to this witness.

John Webster became High Sheriff of Warwickshire in 1754, and when he died in 1768 he was buried at Stoneleigh and a wall monument in his memory placed in Stoneleigh Church. However, a stern lesson of warning is to be learnt by all cattle breeders from his example. Tempted by high prices, he parted with his best stock, so ruining his herd, whereas Bakewell, Prinsep and Fowler, who followed on, kept their best stock to themselves and became justly famous.

Robert Bakewell laid the foundations of his Dishley herd with a couple of the Canley heifers and, like Webster, a Westmorland bull. Through these two original females, there is a direct line to Sir Thomas Gresley's blood and, from Bakewell, that blood was imparted to nearly all the herds in the country.

Another early herd to be mentioned is that of George Chapman of Upton near Nuneaton, Warwickshire, who began to select Longhorns in 1756. These men were the greatest of their generation. They were the outstanding representatives of a small band of livestock improvers who achieved results of inestimable benefit to English farming.

There was certainly a great interchange of blood between Webster, Bakewell and Chapman, and many a ride these old-world worthies must have had across Charnwood, sometimes called Charley Forest. This was once a noted chase and it is written that the monks of the nearby Garendon Abbey once complained of one John Comyn killing a hundred wild hogs in the forest, that number being more than his lawful due. A trial took place according to Druidical laws and the jury gave a verdict against the monks, after which the rights of the chase were divided and the pork-loving Comyn was left to pursue his sport unthreatened by priestly vengeance.

As may be assumed from this story, it must have been no easy matter for strangers to cross this almost pathless wilderness in the days of our Longhorn friends. But no doubt, with the lure of a good animal to be seen at the end of the ride, they made light work of it.

The charms of Charnwood Forest were extolled by Michael Drayton, born in 1563:

> O, Charnwood, be thou called the choicest of thy kind
> The like in any place, what flood hath hapt to find?
> No tract in all this isle, the proudest let her be,
> Can show a sylvan nymph for beauty like to thee!
> The satyrs and the fawns, by Dian set to keep
> Rough hills and forest holts, were sadly seen to weep,
> When thy high palméd harts, the sport of boors and hounds,
> By gripple borderers' hands were banished thy grounds.

This verse gives a small glimpse into an area of 18,000 acres through which our noted Longhorn breeders often travelled. For many famous sons of Longhorn lore lived around the borders of the forest: Bakewell, Buckley and Stone to the north and Knowles, Astley and Paget to the south.

## Letting Out Sires

The improvement in the Midlands was greatly accelerated by hiring out sires for the season. Prior to letting time, the owners held exhibitions of their stock for dairymen and graziers to attend and choose their sires for the coming season. The practice was used for bulls, stallions and rams. There were also public shows in the Midlands for the same purpose. Ashby-de-la-Zouch had its Stallion Show, Leicester its Ram Show and Market Bosworth had its show for bulls. But the sires at these shows were there for selling as well as letting.

The practice of letting meant that, for example, a superior bull, instead of being confined to his owner's herd and those of a few neighbours, became a treasure in which the whole district could share. One year he would be standing in one part of a county and the next year in another part – rather like a circuit judge doing the rounds. In this way one good bull could have an enormous impact on the surrounding countryside and any sons got by him, which shared his good qualities, were also let to circulate his blood still further.

This is the earliest example of a breed structure in which a few famous long-established herds provided highly sought-after bulls for the use of the breed as a whole, or for upgrading local nondescript stock. As a result, by 1810, the overwhelming majority of cattle in the Midland counties were of improved Longhorn type.

Robert Bakewell was the first man to pioneer progeny testing through the letting of his sires. Through a bull, ram or stallion being used on a wide range of females, on different soil types and in different climatic conditions, a more accurate picture of his worth as a sire could be formed. In this way the benefits of a particular animal could be assimilated far sooner than if he were to remain with one small group of females and his worth probably not fully appreciated until after his death.

## Longhorns in Ireland

'For a period of unknown antiquity' Longhorns very much resembling those in England have been found in Ireland. Ancient records are silent on the matter of whether England or Ireland was the native country for the breed, but they can be traced back to a very remote period. Writers in the early 1800s reported that the Longhorn was regarded as an import to Ireland. They were to be found most commonly in the lower and most thickly populated areas, probably being taken over from Lancashire. The middle-horn Kerry was the native breed, being found in every mountainous and unfrequented region.

Robert Wallace, writing in 1885, reported that the herd on the Earl of Westmeath's estate at Pallas, County Galway, was said to have been bred pure for over 200 years, fresh blood being imported from England from time to time. Youatt, writing in 1833, said that the Longhorns were most plentiful in Tipperary, Limerick, Meath and a great part of Munster and, particularly, Roscommon, and that in about 1710, some zealous agriculturists

*The variety of Irish Longhorn. There is no doubt that they very much resembled the English Longhorn, by which they had been materially improved (an engraving by William Youatt, 1838).*

in Meath also started the improvement of the breed. A Mr Waller of Allenstown introduced some of the Old Lancashires at this time. Sixty years later, a relation of his brought over one of the New Leicester breed of cattle. He permitted his neighbours and tenants to have almost unlimited use of this bull and there was scarcely a cottager within three or four miles of Allenstown who did not possess a cow showing some traces of Leicestershire blood. About the same time, Lord Massarene introduced some Longhorn cattle into Antrim.

In 1775, Mr Lesley of Lesley-hill imported one of Bakewell's bulls and the cattle of the neighbouring county were quickly improved. In Langford, the cattle were much improved by the efforts of the Earl of Ross who imported several bulls of 'the best British blood'. On 21 May 1802, he sold ten six-year-old bullocks at the fair at Ballymahoe for 400 guineas and ten four-year-old heifers for 300 guineas. For size, shape and fatness, it was reported, they could not be excelled, and all they had consumed was grass and hay.

Almost every county of Ireland had its successful improver of the Longhorn breed until, it is written, Bakewell himself said that in the richer and more cultivated districts they could even rival the best that the Midland counties of England could produce – excepting those of Bakewell himself. At the fair at Ballinasloe, he found individuals of the breed which he regarded as inferior only to those which he himself had perfected. Bakewell became a considerable exporter of livestock, animals of his breeding being recorded as far afield as America and South Africa.

Robert Bakewell wrote to Arthur Young on 10 March 1788: 'I have sold a bull and two heifers which are to be put on board this week to go to Maryland, N. America and, if they please, I hope to have further orders.'

In 1771, Arthur Young wrote that Bakewell had recently sent many cattle to Ireland.

While on his second visit to Dishley, in 1785, Arthur Young related that Bakewell sold a three-year-old bull, a two-year-old bull and two yearlings to a gentleman in Jamaica who had bought a bull in 1777 which was still in perfect health and vigour, in spite of the change of climate. He had found the breed to suit his requirements so well that he had come again, eight years later, to buy more, having been convinced that the breed was superior to all others of his experience.

In September 1806, Honeybourne, Bakewell's nephew, sent six Dishley rams for letting to Ireland, accompanied by their shepherd. All were drowned when the ship carrying them, the *King George*, was wrecked.

# CHAPTER SEVEN

# The Art of Breeding

The Grand old Longhorn, Bakewell's breed, must ever hold first place in the chronological history of the scientific and systematic improvement of British cattle, and long may the type be preserved in its true grandeur and picturesque beauty.

*(David Lowe, 1842)*

Wiliam Marshall reported that although 'Mr Bakewell has been long and most deservedly considered as the principal promoter of the ART OF BREEDING' and had been 'at the top of the tree for some time', 'the district of the Midland counties abounds with intelligent and spirited breeders'. Marshall said he knew of at least 15 to 20 men of repute, and most of them men of considerable property, who were distinguished for their breeds of stock. Nevertheless, he acknowledged that Robert Bakewell was the head of the department and that 'Whenever he may drop, it is much to be feared, and highly probable, that another leader, of equal spirit, and equal abilities, will not be found to succeed him.'

Marshall goes on to say that, although he had many opportunities to observe Bakewell's practices and had regular communication with him, he was going to maintain the 'reporter's impartiality. It is not my intention to deal out Mr B's private opinions or even attempt a recital of his particular practice.'

Commendable as this ideal may have been then, it is today a great tragedy for us that he felt compelled to speak only in general terms. It is a lost opportunity which would have given us great insight into Bakewell's thoughts and methods.

Before the improvers arrived on the scene, the accepted practice in breeding farm animals was to select females of the native stock of a county and to cross them with bulls of a different breed, as it was believed that continuing to use the same line of parentage weakened the stock. Ernle says that, prior to Bakewell, 'Stock-breeding as applied to both cattle and sheep was the haphazard union of nobody's son with everybody's daughter.'

When the improvers came along they used practices directly contrary. They bred not only from the same line but from the same parentage. The term used at first for the practice was 'breeding in-and-in', and later 'line breeding'. It became the ordinary practice of superior breeders to mate father and daughter, son and mother, brother and sister. It was by these means that Bakewell produced his celebrated stock, for he and his fellow-improvers held the belief that there could be only one best breed, and that if you crossed it you would be doing so with an inferior breed, thus adulterating and not improving.

Marshall, writing in 1790, pointed out that great strides had been made in the livestock breeding of the time by 'breeding in-and-in' and by 'crossing superior branches of the same breed'. The rapidity with which these improvements were made was quite remarkable when compared with the years that had gone before. George Culley said that 'the kind of cattle most esteemed before Mr Bakewell's time were the large, long-bodied, big-boned, coarse, flat-sided kind and often lyery or black fleshed!'

Bakewell's improvements in all manner of farm livestock were little short of magical and they were brought about by the use of line breeding, as has just been mentioned. This went totally against the old and extensively practised idea that no bull should be used on the same stock for more than three years, and no ram for more than two years, otherwise it would lead to deficient offspring. Bakewell had to overcome almost overwhelming resistance to change of any sort. The age-old attitude of 'what was good enough for my father is good enough for me' was predominant. Also, this was a time when, after all, religious beliefs were sacrosanct and Bakewell's breeding policy went against everything the church stood for.

George Culley wrote: 'Some have imbibed the prejudice against Bakewell's breeding practice so far as to think it is irreligious.' This would provide a valid reason for his fabled secretiveness regarding the breeding of his stock, if indeed it existed. It is clear, though, that his methods were passed on to his pupils such as Culley and the Colling brothers for, in using the principles laid down by him, they were even able to surpass him.

However, it was said that, other than his faithful shepherd, a man called Jack Breedon, whom he employed in 1760, no one knew the exact secret of how he obtained such outstanding specimens of the various types of livestock which graced the pastures at Dishley. Breedon played a most active part in the formation of the 'New Leicester' sheep, but the manner in which they were obtained was kept a complete secret.

The goal for which Robert Bakewell strove, both in the production of livestock and in the general management of his farm, was economy. His principal target in cattle breeding was to refine and reduce the bone and offal of a beast and to increase the proportions of consumable meat. He is quoted as saying, 'All is useless that is not flesh', and his ideal was to obtain three-fifths to roast against two-fifths to boil. In his travels, to extend his knowledge of farming practices, he found much to admire in the methods used by the farmers of Norfolk and, from abroad, those of Holland and Flanders who were characterised by their efficiency and thrift. It was upon these principles of management that Bakewell is believed to have founded his own system at Dishley.

The many visitors to Dishley gave accounts of 'scrupulous neatness, order, ingenious time-saving devices and the economic ways of efficiently carrying out the ordinary work of the farm'. In other words, in every way rigid economy was practised. In view of the path that Bakewell was destined to walk, this was no bad thing, for the many and varied experiments which he was to conduct were to prove both costly and time-consuming. The more successful the farm, the better able it was to support the testing of Bakewell's theories.

Bakewell's decision to adopt the already well-established cattle breed of the Midlands, the Longhorn, was not taken lightly. He tried many breeds before deciding that the Longhorn was capable of doing better in Leicestershire than any other breed.

So his work of improvement began, work which had already

been started for him by the likes of Sir Thomas Gresley of Drakelow and the Websters of Canley. For, although he had not been there when the first seeds were sown, he certainly had the imagination to use knowledge from those who had gone before and carry it to its conclusion. The original, pre-1700s Longhorn had been a slow-growing, slow-moving, lean-fleshed creature which was light in the hindquarters and a fair but not outstanding milker. The breed which Bakewell took on had already risen to a high degree of advancement in both its beefing and dairying qualities.

An idea of the improvements to livestock, brought about by Bakewell, can be seen by the following figures quoted by Ernle, of the average weights of sheep and cattle sold at Smithfield Market in 1710 and 1795. In 1710 the average weight for beeves was

*A Longhorn bred by Mr Minion of Stedford, near Tamworth, the property of T. S. Burgess of Holmepierrpoint, Notts. This animal was ten years old when exhibited at Smithfield in December 1839 and won the first prize of 20 sovereigns as the best fatted cow of five years and over (from* Farmer's Magazine, *April 1840).*

370 lb, for calves 50 lb, for sheep 28 lb and for lambs 18 lb. In
1795 beeves had risen in average weight to 800 lb, calves to
148 lb, sheep to 80 lb and lambs to 50 lb.

Although no record survives to tell us exactly how Bakewell
achieved his ultimate goal, we must assume that he started by
breeding from animals as close to his ideal as he could find. By
breeding them in-and-in, he fixed in them those characteristics
that he esteemed the most. It is known that Bakewell kept four
principal points steadfastly in mind:

1. Breed
2. Utility and beauty of form (to include fineness of bone, light-
   ness of offal and the greater weight in the best parts).
3. Quality of flesh (a point which had not before been considered
   by breeders).
4. Disposition to fatten.

## Robert Bakewell's Longhorns

It has always been acknowledged as a fact that Robert Bakewell
started his herd of Longhorns by the purchase of one red and one
yellow heifer from Mr Webster of Canley, Warwickshire,* and a
bull from Westmorland. The often-quoted line 'From these pure
Longhorns he bred the whole of his herd' has been passed on from
one writer to another down the years. However, when one
considers this statement, it seems certain that there must have been
cattle at Dishley before the Webster Longhorns were introduced
and they must surely have been of the long-established breed of
the area, the Longhorn.

An interesting disclosure by Arthur Young related the following, published in 1811: 'I learn from Mr Culley that some errors
have been afloat relative to the origin of Bakewell's cattle, the
chief merit of which has been assigned to the stock of Mr Webster
of Canley; but this stock were in several ways inferior to the

---

* Information given on a sale catalogue for the sale of Mr Wyatt's cattle, in 1840, to
Mr Nugent.

yellow breed, before at Dishley. They were greatly deficient in disposition or propensity to make readily fat, which the yellow cattle were so eminently possessed of.'

As we have already observed, Longhorns, although the most predominant of the breeds throughout the Midland counties, took on localised characteristics, colour being one of them. We know that one of the heifers purchased by Bakewell, from Mr Webster, was of yellow colouration. It is purely conjecture, but could she have been picked out by Bakewell not only for her breeding ability, but also because she was of a colour favoured by him, and already to be seen at home? He is on record as having said that 'Pale colours indicate finer meat than darker ones.'

This quotation from Arthur Young is the first mention we have found that there were superior cattle at Dishley *before* the purchase from Webster, although the area was already well known as a stronghold of the breed. If it is true that Bakewell was in possession of superior stock before the Webster purchases, he is much maligned by his detractors who allege that he gained the glory for Webster's deeds.

There are also two conflicting stories of how Bakewell's famous bull, Twopenny, was bred. The first and most widespread is that his dam was one of the two heifers bought from Webster, the heifer later known as Old Comely. Comely was born in 1765, and lived to the great age of 26 years. According to Pitt, writing in 1809, 'She died when life had become burdensome to her.' She is known historically as Old Comely, and years after her death parts of her were still to be seen, preserved in the hall at Dishley, which Bakewell kept as a museum. It is recorded that her sirloin was 4 in. thick.

Bakewell kept pickled joints and skeletons of his best stock in order to compare one generation with another – ancestors with their descendants. The fineness of bone, size and shape of frame, thickness of muscle layer and depth of outside fat were all factors he compared. All this information was recorded to serve as a guide. It must have greatly helped Bakewell's assessment of the living animals, enabling more accurate estimates of their value for breeding purposes.

A visitor to Dishley named Throsby described Old Comely in 1790 as standing 'like a venerable ruin on props of magnificent architecture, bulging fine limbs, enfeebled with age. I will not attempt to describe what she has been, only in general terms observe that she is now twenty-five years old, and has been esteemed by judges as one of the finest animals of that species ever bred. She now lives in an asylum, a meadow full of keep, set apart to smooth her passage to the earth, for in the slaughterhouse she is not to make her exit. She eats but little and yet retains upon her back, which is now a yard over, broad cushions of fat. She seldom moves. She stood like a statue while I went round her, upon her legs bowed at the joint like those of a decrepit old man in the last stage of his existence.'

The other story about the illustrious bull Twopenny was that he was out of a cow bought by Bakewell from Sir William Gordon of Garrington. Gordon was married to the widow Phillips, of the Garendon estate, of which Dishley was a part. (Garrington is clearly a corruption of the name Garendon.)

Arthur Young, who saw Twopenny in 1770, described him as being 'a very big bull, most truly made, on the barrel principle, circular, but broad across the back'. He also stated that Bakewell refused an offer of 200 guineas for the bull.

A fee of 5 guineas per cow was charged for the service of Twopenny, standing at Dishley, but his sons could be hired for the season for between 5 and 30 guineas. In later years Bakewell was to relinquish his hold on his pride and joy for a while by letting both Mr Chapman of Upton, Nuneaton, Warwickshire, and Mr Fowler of Little Rollright, Oxfordshire, hire him for a season each.

Bakewell bred his Longhorns in-and-in as a means of fixing the type he desired for beef production. Being fully aware of the risks attached to such a course, he was prepared to face the consequences and cull hard where necessary. Lowe recorded that 'Amid many disappointments he never despaired of his ultimate purpose, but bore up against ridicule, neglect and predictions of failure till the end.' Nevertheless, Bakewell's practice was not solely one of inbreeding but one of breeding *mostly* from within his own group of whichever type of animal he was dealing with. Occasionally he bred from closely related animals, but also sometimes from unrelated animals.

The resulting cattle of his long endeavours were exceptional for their fineness of bone and excellent fleshing qualities. A contemporary description of them is:

> Sound, tight, cylindrical carcase, wide in the hips but with very
> little prominence of the huckle bones, straight back, well-filled
> behind the shoulders, neck long and fine without any superfluous
> skin or dewlap, horns long, tapering downwards, and of a deep
> yellowish colour, head fine and smooth. The barrel form,
> gradually tapering towards the ends, was the model, as also in the
> sheep. The cattle being peculiarly light in the belly and offal.

Marshall described Robert Bakewell as being in possession of many valuable individuals:

> His bull, D, generally being known by the name of the 'Mad
> Bull', is a fine animal and is striking proof of the vulgar error that
> breeding in-and-in weakens the breed. He was got by a son of
> Twopenny out of a daughter and sister of the same celebrated
> bull, she being the produce of his own dam. D is the sire of
> Shakespeare which is out of another daughter by the same bull,
> and is probably the most robust individual of the Longhorn
> breed, while D himself at the age of 12 or 13 years, is more alive
> and higher mettled than bulls in general are at the age of three or
> four years old. This has long been esteemed Bakewell's best bull
> and has been kept principally for his own use. He was never let
> except part of a season to Mr Fowler but has individual cows
> brought to him at five guineas each. The hindquarters of the bull
> D are quite remarkable, his tail appearing to grow out of the top
> of his spine, rather than be a continuation of his vertebrae, the
> upper part of the tail forming an arch which rises some inches
> above the general level of the back, making him spectacular to
> view, but from the point of the grazier a bad one, as it tended to
> hide the fatness of the rump. Mr Bakewell's cows are of the finest
> mould and the highest quality and his heifers beautiful as taste
> could well conceive them, clean and active as does. Mr
> Bakewell's exhibition of cattle would gratify the most indifferent
> spectator and could not fail of being highly satisfactory to every
> lover of the rural science.

Marshall also said that 'Some of the Dishley heifers have shoulders as fine as racehorses.'

Youatt described the Dishley Longhorn as being 'unrivalled for the soundness of its horn, the smallness of its bone, and the aptitude to acquire external fat', while being small consumers of feed in proportion to their size, but at the same time their qualities as milkers were considerably lessened. 'The grazier could not too highly value the Dishley or New Leicester Longhorn but the dairyman and the little farmers clung to the old breed as most useful for their purpose.'

In his second visit to Dishley, in 1785, Arthur Young noticed considerable 'improvement' had taken place with the Longhorn. This consisted of the development of enormous masses of fat over the hip bones and around the tail head. Formerly Bakewell had been content to breed animals heavy in the hindquarters, now he was breeding for abnormal, almost grotesque, protuberances of fat. This at the time was seen as a most desirable point for, until this advent, the great difficulty had been to breed animals that would fatten easily. The working man's diet being very poor, fat meat then formed an essential part of it. Fat also provided a large part of the energy intake for rich and poor alike in the days when physical activity, including walking, was a much larger part of life than now. Fat by-products like tallow also added to the value of an animal, because of their use to provide oil for light when no other was available.

Young recorded that the hip bones of one cow were 'buried in a mound of fat fourteen inches in diameter, but she continued to calve yearly'. High condition was the rule of the day in the breeding herd at Dishley and Young went on to describe the cattle as being 'fat as bears' and 'if the degree of fatness in which he keeps all these cattle be considered, and that he buys neither straw nor hay, it must appear that he keeps a larger stock on a given number of acres than most men in England.'

William Pitt's description of two bulls he viewed at Dishley in 1809, under the ownership of Bakewell's nephew, Mr Honeybourne, who retained the farm after the death of his uncle was: 'As fine in the bone, clean-made and free from offal, and from every appearance of coarseness as many heifers.' This description is enforced by the images portrayed by the painters of the period, who painted true to life and had not been touched by the later fashion of the mid-19th century to exaggerate an animal's form for the gratification of the proud owner.

The description of the bull, D, giving details of the abnormally high tail head as a point, would be frowned upon today. The Longhorn has come a long way to be accepted in today's world, with our greatly different standards.

The following is a description of the Improved Leicester Longhorn of Bakewellian fame, as written by William Marshall:

> The FOREND long but light to a degree of elegance. The neck thin, the chap clean, the head fine but long and tapering. The EYE large, bright and prominent. The HORNS vary with the sex, those of oxen are extremely large being from two and a half to three feet long, those of the cows are nearly as long but much finer, tapering to delicately fine points. Most of them hang downwards by the side of the cheeks and, if well turned, as many of the cows are, shoot forward at the points.★ The SHOULDERS remarkably fine and thin, as to bone, but thickly covered with flesh, with not the smallest protuberance discernable. The Dishley cattle excelling in this point, having shoulders as fine as racehorses. The GIRTH small compared with the Shorthorn and middle-horn breeds, although Mr Fowler's cattle were well let down in the girth. The CHINE remarkably full when fat but hollow when low in condition. The LOIN broad and the HIP remarkably wide and protuberant. The QUARTERS long and level. The ROUNDBONES small but the THIGHS in general fleshy. The LEGS small and clean but comparatively long. The feet in general neat. The CARCASE as near a cylinder as the natural form of the animal will allow. The RIBS standing out full from the spine, the BELLY small. The FLESH seldom fails to be of the first quality. The HIDE of middle thickness. The COLOUR various, the brindle, the finch back and the pye are common. The paler they are the better they seem to be in esteem.

★ Those of the bulls being comparatively short, from 15 in. to 2 ft.

An anonymous journalist, writing for a newspaper after visiting Dishley soon after Paget's great sale in 1793, recorded: 'The famous white bull is a noble animal but I found many preferred that sold at the Paget's sale.' Does this suggest that the term 'white', when used by a layman, meant a pale roan? Alas, we shall never know. The Paget bull mentioned is obviously the son of Shakespeare, which lived up to his expectations when he realised the price of 400 guineas.

*Melcombe at two years old. Bred by J. H. Burbery, he was the property of James Davis of Melcombe, Horsey, Dorchester, and the winner of the first prizes at the Battersea and Worcester meetings of the RASE in 1862 and 1863.*

Bakewell conducted many experiments throughout his life with all forms of livestock to ascertain the return they gave him on his capital expenditure. As well as testing one Longhorn against another, he also pitted Longhorns against other breeds. As the results always ended in favour of the Longhorn, they confirmed for him that the path he had chosen was the right one. Although none of the records of these experiments have survived in his own hand, we have to be indebted to Messrs Young, Marshall and Pitt who tell us that no one ever made more comparisons between the different breeds of cattle than Bakewell and, accordingly, 'No one that was able to tell us so much, has told us so little.'

Bakewell did not make public the results of his own experiments, his reasoning being that as they were carried out by his own men on his own farm, they would be invalid to anyone other than himself, for fear that he would be accused of loading the results in his own favour. Young, writing in 1771, remarked that 'Mr Bakewell has several comparisons between other breeds of cattle and his own which I purposely omit taking notice of because such experiments are impossible to be accurate from the great differences in certain breeds in feeding, fattening, etc. Besides, supposing such accuracy, still other people, and particularly those of the countries compared, would never give credit to such comparisons unless the very best breeders in the very best countries themselves chose certain beasts to represent their breed. Nor does Mr Bakewell's breed want any such experiments to recommend them.'

In his letters to George Culley, Bakewell expressed the wish that Arthur Young should not be so open in praising him to the press, fearing that it would only help to alienate him from the rest of the farming community, and so damage his cause for the progression of agriculture. This reveals the modest and sensitive side to his nature.

The following is just one of the many and varied trials carried out at Dishley. Three newly calved cows were individually housed – a Holderness, a Scotch and a Longhorn. The Holderness ate the most food and gave the greatest quantity of milk. The Scotch ate less food and gave less milk but produced the most butter, while the Longhorn ate the least food, gave the least milk and butter but laid on the most flesh, thus proving that the Dishley cattle were best adapted for the needs of the grazier in the production of beef.

Always one to be thinking of practicality, a most forward-thinking innovation of Bakewell's was to use his three-year-old heifers for draught purposes, replacing the traditional oxen which were then released from their labours for the purpose of slaughter. Bakewell thought oxen the most unprofitable animals to keep and only retained exceptional specimens for draught or slaughter. Bull calves were generally fattened and killed for veal at around two months of age, producing 160 pounds of veal. He felt that more profit could be gained from fattening and killing heifers either before or after their first calf, compared to the costly practice of keeping oxen for slaughter. As soon as heifers came to breeding age they were broken to the yoke, calving for the first time well into their fourth year, this being the accepted age at the time, because it was thought best for the health and strength of both cow and calf. Draught cattle were kept stalled throughout the year, just like horses, and in the summer fed on mown grass while in the winter they had a diet of straw or hay with turnips or cabbages. They were used for all the light carting work, the heavier tasks usually being left to horses. Heifers were easily trained and managed and from twelve to twenty of them were constantly ready for use. Three of them would work a plough or cart, and they were found to be most tractable and docile. They could work for up to nine hours a day, usually from 6.00 a.m. to noon and, after a two-hour rest, from 2.00 to 5.00 p.m.

Bakewell devised a cattle crush specifically to aid in the shoeing of oxen and heifers, the largest specimens being easily dealt with in this manner. He is said to have refused the sum of 120 guineas for a working team of six heifers.

In all Marshall's travels, Bakewell was the only man of his acquaintance to keep cows solely for the purpose of rearing their own offspring. Elsewhere, with the cows' milk being required for the manufacture of cheese, calves were butchered either at birth or at four days old and sold for the price of three or four shillings. A ready market for the meat was to be found in manufacturing towns or collieries. Replacement stock were reared by two methods. In the first, the calves were left on a cow for anything from six to twelve months of age, a cow of little value being bought for the purpose. Such a cow would generally rear either one bull calf or two heifer calves. The second and more usual way was to allow the calf to suck from a cow for one to two weeks before being transferred to bucket rearing. The bucket feed was gradually changed from whole milk to a mixture of skimmed milk and ground oats. In periods of milk scarcity, calves in some areas were kept quiet by being dosed with three paste balls the size of walnuts, made from wheat flour and gin. These were administered fifteen minutes before a feed and kept the animals in a comatose state most of the time. Calves were reared on the bucket for up to four months.

When we summarise the contribution made by Bakewell to the Longhorn breed we find they were capable of growing fat on less food than the original stock. They fattened quickly and in more valuable parts of the body, and the flesh itself was improved in its eating qualities. They retained their ability to withstand harsh conditions and poor pasture, justifying Bakewell's faith in the Longhorn to keep itself in good condition on less food than other cattle of equal weight. The only drawback to his practice was the loss of ability to produce enough milk for the dairy. This one point made the choice of the Longhorn untenable for the small farmers of the day. They required a dual-purpose animal and therefore clung to the old, unimproved type.

When compared to the animals we have today, and the aims we are striving to achieve, the considerations of those days are entirely different. The need for fat meat in Bakewell's time has been wholly eclipsed nowadays by the call for leaner and yet leaner carcases. Today's fashion is for an animal of large proportions, requiring a good frame and bone, with bulls needing to show width, depth and quality, including being level in the back and sound of foot. Good hindquarter development is, of course, keenly sought.

Arthur Young once said of Bakewell: 'I am proud to be able to pay a tribute of respect to the memory of this great man who by his genius has created and scattered over the green hills and verdant meadows of his native land an animal whose beauty and usefulness will ever be a living monument to record his name.'

Bakewell may be said to be the first agricultural patriot, 'for the man who endeavours by incessant exertions to improve the animal creation is as fully deserving of that distinctive appellation, as is the statesman whose exertions are employed in human rights' (*Farmer's Magazine*, August 1842).

# CHAPTER EIGHT

# Breeders After Bakewell

His celebrity as a Longhorn breeder will ever shed a halo over his name.

The lack of national recognition of the achievements of Robert Bakewell has been a subject of comment for many years. The following appeared in the *Farmer's Magazine* of August 1842:

> Memoirs of utilitarians are very seldom written. The quiet tenor of their lives, unlike the glare of that which sheds a halo around the heads of the warrior and the statesman, affords but little field, for the display of the talents of the biographer. Hence it is, that the real benefactors of mankind are but too frequently passed over in silence, and we walk over the green sward that finishes where the remains of those energies were devoted to the improvement of the race of animals, that contribute largely to add to the creature comforts of man, and moulder into primitive dust, without even thinking that we tread on hallowed soil, for the earth beneath which a good man rests, is hallowed in the remembrance of his virtues and his usefulness.
>
> Mr Bakewell has been strangely neglected by those who ought to have been his warmest and most grateful advocates. But such is the way of the world, neglect, almost universally, is the reward of merit.
>
> Cultivators naturally look to the amount of profits that are likely to arise from the practice of any separate system. Those of Bakewell did not place him among the wealthy, but had he been less liberal with his ideas, less given to hospitality, less visited by the patrician portion of the community, who entailed enormous

expenses upon him, he must have lived and died a rich man, whether it was his desire to do so or not. A practical agriculturist is of far more value to the nation than even a practical manufacturer, for the benefit the one confers upon the human race are lasting – the other but transient, yet both deserve to be honoured by their country . . .

It ought to be remarked that the liberality, generosity and high mindedness of Mr Bakewell never evinced itself more fully than in his incessant application to the improvement of Dishley estate. He was but a tenant but he yearly increased the value of the land he rented for the benefit of the landlord.

For two hundred years we have subconsciously followed Robert Bakewell's methods, and the breeds we have today have been cultivated with the use of the knowledge we have gained from him. Arthur Young, writing after Bakewell's death, said, 'His system was established with such completeness that men forgot not only the existence of any different conditions but even the very name of the most active pioneer of change.'

## Robert Fowler

Of the many breeders who followed hot on the heels of Bakewell, Robert Fowler, of Little Rollright on the borders of Oxfordshire and Warwickshire, became the most prominent. After purchasing two cows from Mr Webster and hiring Bakewell's bull Twopenny he set the seal on what was to be one of the most successful and famous herds in English agricultural history, second only to Bakewell's, for when his Rollright herd of Longhorns was eventually put under the hammer it was to become the first pedigree cattle sale ever recorded.

Robert Parry of Shipston-on-Stour, writing on 14 May 1791, informed us that from the mating of the Webster cows with Twopenny came the famed matriarchs of his herd, Old Long-horned Beauty and Old Nell. He hired several bulls from Dish-ley, finally ending with D in 1778, a very inbred grandson of Twopenny. Fowler sealed the fortune of his herd when he bred Shakespeare who was by D, the grandson of Twopenny, out of a daughter of Twopenny. From this point on he never looked outside his own herd for sires. Shakespeare was to occupy a position among the Longhorns equivalent to Favourite and Comet in later years among the Shorthorn tribe.

William Marshall, writing in 1790, gives us the following description of Shakespeare and the Rollright herd.

> This bull is a striking specimen of what naturalists term accidental varieties. Although he is greatly inbred he scarcely inherits a single point of the Longhorn breed except for his horns. When I first saw him in 1784, then 6 years old, and somewhat below his usual condition, though by no means low in flesh, he was of this description.
>
> His head, chap and neck, remarkably fine and clean. His chest extraordinarily deep, his brisket down to his knees. His chine thin and rising above the shoulder points, leaving a hollow on each side, behind them. His loin of course narrow at the chine but remarkably wide at the hips, which protuberate in a singular manner. His quarters long in reality, but in appearance short occasioned by a singular formation of rump. At first sight it appears as if the tail, which stands forward, had been severed from the vertebrae by the chop of a cleaver, one of the vertebrae extracted and the tail forced up to make good the joint, an appearance which on examining is occasioned by some remarkable wreaths of fat formed round the setting-on of the tail, a circumstance which in a picture would be deemed a deformity, but as a point is in the highest esteem. The round bones snug but the thighs rather full and remarkably let down. The legs short and their bone fine. The carcase throughout (the chine excepted) large, roomy, deep and well spread. His horns apart, he had every point of a Holderness or a Teeswater bull. Could his horns have been changed he would have passed in Yorkshire as an ordinary bull of either of these breeds. His two ends would have been thought tolerably good but his middle very deficient, and I am of the opinion that had he been put to cows of these breeds his stock would have been of moderate quality, but being put to cows deficient where he was full (the lower part of the thigh excepted) and full where he was deficient, he has raised the Longhorn breed to a degree of perfection which, without so extraordinary a prodigy, they might never have reached.
>
> No wonder that a form so uncommon should strike the improvers of this breed of stock, or that a carcase they have been so long striving in vain to produce, should be rated at a high

price. His owner, however, being among the first of his admirers, could never be induced to part with him, even for a season, except to Mr Prinsep who had him two seasons, at the extraordinary price of 80 guineas a season. A price at which no other bull has yet been let.

This remakable animal is now [1789] 11 years old and firm in his constitution, but so lame in his hindquarters as to render him at present and during the last season useless.

In 1793 a bull called Shakespeare was sold at the dispersal sale of Mr T. Paget of Ibstock, Leicestershire, for the sum of 400 guineas. Although in recent years it was assumed that this was the Shakespeare of Mr Fowler's, the above statement of his lameness gave little credence to the tale, and on finding the records of the Paget sale it was seen that the bull sold in 1793 was bred by Fowler, by his bull Shakespeare out of Young Nell. He was bought by a syndicate of local gentlemen and the price which was paid indicates the great regard which was held for his sire. The gentlemen after their purchase charged 25 guineas per cow for his services, but Paget retained the right to send two cows to him yearly.

Fowler was left in a very strong position after the passing of Shakespeare. He had many valuable females by him and also one bull by the name of Garrick, whose dam had been got by Robert Bakewell's Hampshire Bull.

Marshall witnessed 25 cows at Fowler's and found many of them to be of an extraordinary stamp, especially in the fineness of the fore-end and the width and fatness of the hindquarters. 'A daughter and sister of Shakespeare being got on his own dam, is amongst the best of his herd, another evidence of the good effect of breeding from the same family.'

Initially Fowler conducted his business on the old principles of selling, and not the new way of letting. He not only sold his surplus bulls, but also heifers that were not required for his own dairy purposes. During the years 1785–89 Mr Coke of Norfolk had all the heifer calves he could spare at 10 guineas each, and in October 1789 he declined an offer of 500 guineas for ten bull calves by Garrick.

During the latter part of his life Fowler would not part with a good cow as long as she continued to breed, refusing at one point 1,000 guineas for three cows and a bull, probably as a direct result of the regret he always felt for a transaction he made in the year 1771 with Mr Guy of Taddington. Mr Guy then purchased three heifers by Twopenny for 80 guineas as the foundation stock for his herd, and although unfortunate in the choice of some bulls, which he afterwards made use of, and therefore not so successful as he might otherwise have been, the prices of his stock at his dispersal sale in April 1790 are enough to convince us of their superiority to most others, with some of his cows by a bull of Mr Fowler's selling for up to 40 guineas.

Fowler, regretting his sale to Mr Guy, almost immediately offered to buy back one of the heifers, The Painted Lady, at the amount he had received for the three, but to no avail.

'The Arab sticks to his mare no more lovingly than does Mr Fowler to his Longhorn Queens,' said Marshall, but time and tide wait for no man – and so it was eventually the auctioneer's hammer that broke the bond between Fowler and the mothers of his herd. The following is a most true and exact record of this historic sale of pedigree stock.

The Celebrated Stock of Mr Robert Fowler, of Little Rollright, in the County of Oxford, which was Submitted to the Hammer 29, 30 and 31 March 1791

| Lot | BULLS | £ | s | d |
|---|---|---|---|---|
| 1 | GARRICK, 5 yrs, by Shakespeare, out of Broken Beauty. Mr Stone, Quorndon, Leics. | 215 | 5 | 0 |
| 2 | SULTAN, 2 yrs, by Shakespeare, dam Broken Horn Beauty. Messrs Freeman, Eden, of Norton, Glos. | 220 | 10 | 0 |
| 3 | WASHINGTON, 2 yrs, by Shakespeare, dam Bow Horn Red Cow. Mr Buckley, Normanton, Notts. | 215 | 5 | 0 |
| 4 | YOUNG TWOPENNY, 2 yrs, by Garrick, dam Long Horn Beauty. Messrs Cox, Harrison, Macey, Leics. | 68 | 5 | 0 |
| 5 | YOUNG GARRICK, 1 yr, by Garrick, dam Pillion Rump alias Old Skew Horns. Mr J. Smith, Warwicks. (Purchased for Mr Fowler) | 49 | 7 | 0 |

## COWS

| | | | | |
|---|---|---|---|---|
| 6 | YOUNG BRINDLED BEAUTY, 2 yrs, by Shakespeare, dam Brindled Beauty. Mr Russell, Warwicks. (for Messrs Knowles & Co.) | 66 | 3 | 0 |
| 7 | PILLION RUMP alias OLD SKEW HORNS, by Hampshire Bull, dam Daughter of Ralph. Mr Millington, Wilts. (for Mr Fowler) | 23 | 2 | 0 |
| 8 | BULL CALF by Garrick, dam Pillion Rump. Mr Baker, Farmcot, Glos. | 25 | 4 | 0 |
| 9 | GREAT BRINDLED COW, by D, dam Pillion Rump. Mr Millington, Wilts. (for Mr Fowler) | 31 | 10 | 0 |
| 10 | NELL, by Sampson, dam Old Nell. In calf to Sultan. Mr W. Freeman, Hitcot, Glos. | 38 | 17 | 0 |

(Nell, a daughter of Old Nell (which was a daughter of Twopenny), for the time she has bred, which has not been more than 8 years, has made over 1,000 gns of herself and her stock, which is more than was ever made by any cow in the kingdom, and was highly esteemed with Mr Fowler as some of the best breeding on his farm.)

| | | | | |
|---|---|---|---|---|
| 11 | NELL'S BULL CALF, by Garrick. Mr Joseph Allcock, Longborough, Glos. | 45 | 3 | 0 |
| 12 | NELL'S WHITE BACK, 3 yrs, by Garrick, dam Old Nell. Lord Harborough, Leics. | 89 | 5 | 0 |
| 13 | YOUNG BRIND, 3 yrs, by Garrick, dam Old Nell's Daughter. Lot 41. In calf to Washington. Mr William, Huckvale, Over Norton, Oxon. | 32 | 11 | 0 |
| 14 | A BULL NAMED C, 1 yr, by Garrick, dam Short Tails Daughter, alias The White Back'd Cow. Lot 48. Mr James Moore, Charlcote, Warwicks. [This bull was supposed to be the best of the yearlings but unfortunately met with an accident before the sale.] | 52 | 10 | 0 |
| 15 | LONG HORN'D BEAUTY, by her own brother, dam Long Horns out of Old Beauty. Mr Francis Robbins, Lillington, Warwicks. | 44 | 2 | 0 |
| 16 | LONG HORN'D BEAUTY'S cow calf, by Garrick. Mr Richard Robbins, Lillington, Warwicks. | 22 | 1 | 0 |

| | | | | |
|---|---|---|---|---|
| 17 | NANCY, by Shakespeare, dam a daughter of D with bull calf by Garrick.<br>Mr Brookes, Wolvers Hill, Warwicks. | 52 | 10 | 0 |
| 18 | BRINDLED SHORT TAIL, by Shakespeare, dam a daughter of Old Short Tail. In calf to Garrick.<br>Mr Paget, Ibstock, Leics. | 43 | 1 | 0 |
| 19 | BEAUTY, by Shakespeare, dam Old Long Horns Daughter. In calf to Garrick.<br>Mr John Millington, Wilts. (for Mr Fowler) | 52 | 10 | 0 |
| 20 | A MOTTLED YRLING CALF, by Garrick, dam Long Horn'd Nancy.<br>Mr John Zouch, Millcote, Warwicks. | 27 | 6 | 0 |
| 21 | YOUNG BEAUTY, of Lot 19, a yrling calf, by Garrick, dam Beauty, which is grand-daughter of Old Long Horned Beauty.<br>(Mr Russell for Messrs Knowles & Co.) | 34 | 13 | 0 |
| 22 | A LIGHT COLOURED WELSH NURSE COW.<br>Mr Richard Leythall (for Mr Fowler). | 8 | 8 | 0★ |

## BULLS

| | | | | |
|---|---|---|---|---|
| 23 | YOUNG SHAKESPEARE, 1 yr, by Garrick, dam Daughter of the Short Tailed cow alias Douk Horn.<br>Mr Leythall (for Mr Fowler). | 29 | 8 | 0 |
| 24 | A, 1 yr, by Garrick, dam Brindled Finch. Lot 46, daughter of the Great Brindled cow. Lord Harborough, Leics. | 157 | 10 | 0 |
| 25 | B, 1 yr, by Garrick, dam The Blue Heifer. Lot 45, daughter of the Great Brindled cow. Mr W. Seaton, Scasby, Yorks. | 85 | 1 | 0 |
| 26 | YOUNG SULTAN, 1 yr, by Garrick, dam Nell, Lot 10. Messrs Cox, Harrison, Macey, Leics. | 210 | 0 | 0 |
| 27 | D, 1 yr, by Garrick, dam a daughter of Short Tails.<br>Mr Thomas Clarke, Lockington, Leics. | 88 | 4 | 0 |
| 28 | E, 1 yr, by Garrick, dam Nancy.<br>Mr J. Zouch, Milcote, Warwicks. | 152 | 5 | 0 |
| 29 | F, 1 yr, by Garrick, dam bow horned red cow alias Washington's mother.<br>Mr Francis Robbins, Lillington, Warwicks. | 105 | 0 | 0 |

★ [This lot shows what the ordinary cow was fetching.]

## COWS

| | | | | |
|---|---|---|---|---|
| 30 | BRINDLED BEAUTY, by Shakespeare, dam<br>Long Horned Beauty, she also being dam<br>of Shakespeare (served by Garrick).<br>Mr Russell (for Messrs Knowles & Co.) | 273 | 0 | 0 |
| 31 | GARRICK'S SISTER, by Shakespeare, dam<br>Garrick's mother, alias Broken Horn<br>Beauty (served by Garrick).<br>Mr Russell (for Messrs Knowles & Co.) | 120 | 15 | 0 |
| 32 | WASHINGTON'S MOTHER, by a son of old<br>D, brother to Shakespeare, dam Nell (served<br>by Garrick).<br>Mr Astley, Odstone Hall, Leics. | 194 | 5 | 0 |
| 33 | LONG HORN'D NANCY, by Shakespeare,<br>dam Daughter of Old Nell (in calf to Garrick).<br>Mr W. Freeman, Hitcot, Glos. | 110 | 5 | 0 |
| 34 | SPOTTED NANCY, by Shakespeare, dam<br>Daughter of Old Nell (served by Garrick).<br>Mr Millington, Wilts. (for Mr Fowler) | 84 | 0 | 0 |
| 35 | BLACK HEIFER, 3 yrs, by Shakespeare, dam<br>Brindled Beauty.<br>Mr Russell (for Messrs Knowles & Co.) | 141 | 15 | 0 |
| 36 | GARRICK'S DAUGHTER, 3 yrs, dam<br>Garrick's mother Broken Horn Beauty<br>(served by Sultan).<br>Mr Cox, Brailsford, Derbys. | 47 | 5 | 0 |
| 37 | YOUNG NELL, by a brother of Shakespeare,<br>dam Old Nell (served by Garrick).<br>Mr J. Moore, Charlcote, Warwicks. | 126 | 0 | 0 |
| 38 | YOUNG NELL'S COW CALF, by Garrick.<br>Lord Harborough, Leics. | 31 | 10 | 0 |
| 39 | BROKEN HORN'D BEAUTY, (dam of<br>Garrick and Sultan) by The Hampshire Bull,<br>dam Old Long Horn Beauty (dam of<br>Shakespeare and Lot 30) (served by Garrick).<br>Mr Eden, Norton, Glos. | 46 | 4 | 0 |
| 40 | RED COW, by Shakespeare, dam Old Skew<br>Horns alias Pillion Rump (in calf to Garrick).<br>Mr Cox, Brailsford, Derbys. | 76 | 13 | 0 |
| 41 | NELL'S DAUGHTER, by Shakespeare,<br>Mr Russell, Warwicks. (for Messrs<br>Knowles & Co.) | 136 | 10 | 0 |

| | | | | |
|---|---|---|---|---|
| 42 | COW CALF, by Garrick, dam above. Lord Harborough, Leics. | 43 | 1 | 0 |
| 43 | SALL, by Shakespeare, dam Old Sall (in calf to Garrick). Mr Richard Robbins, Lillington, Warwicks. | 63 | 0 | 0 |
| 44 | DOUK HORN, by Shakespeare, dam Old Short Tail (with cow calf by Garrick). Mr E. Higgins, Old Stratford, Warwicks. | 81 | 18 | 0 |
| 45 | BLUE HEIFER, 4 yrs, by Shakespeare, dam The Great Brindled Cow (with bull calf by Garrick). (Mr Samuel Huckvale, Choice Hill, Oxon.) | 110 | 5 | 0 |
| 46 | BRINDLED FINCH (dam of Lot 24), by Shakespeare, dam The Great Brindled Cow. Mr Eden, Norton, Glos. | 42 | 0 | 0 |
| 47 | BRINDLED FINCH'S COW CALF, by Garrick. Mr Baker, Farmcote, Glos. | 19 | 19 | 0 |
| 48 | WHITE BACK'D COW (dam of Lot 14), by Shakespeare's brother, dam a daughter of the Short tail cow. Mr Eden, Norton, Glos. | 81 | 18 | 0 |
| 49 | COW CALF of WHITE BACK, by Garrick. Mr S. Huckvale, Choice Hill, Oxon. | 32 | 11 | 0 |
| 50 | WHITE BACK'D BROCKEN HORN HEIFER, 2 yrs, by Shakespeare, dam a daughter of Old Nell. Mr Freeman, Hitcot, Glos. | 52 | 10 | 0 |
| 51 | BROKEN HORN, 2 yrs, by Garrick, dam The Great Brindled Cow. Mr W. Seaton, Scasby, Yorks. | 69 | 6 | 0 |
| 52 | A Welsh red nurse cow. | 8 | 18 | 6 |
| 53 | A red and white nurse cow | 11 | 0 | 0 |

At the request of some friends of Fowler, and for others wishing to possess a copy of the extraordinary sale, a reprint was devised by the auctioneer in May 1791. It did not go to print until a full 66 years later, in 1857. The probable reason for this was that, just after the sale, requests were made for the reprint to carry copies of engravings taken from paintings Fowler had commissioned of his cattle. This proving difficult, the task was shelved. It is also worth noting that the stock not only produced the extraordinary prices shown at the sale, but that offers of a considerable advance were made afterwards to many of the purchasers.


# Thomas Paget

In 1793 Mr Thomas Paget of Ibstock, Leicestershire, on deciding to retire to a smaller farm at Market Harborough, put his herd of highly improved Longhorns up for sale by auction. The following prices were achieved:

First Day's Sale, 14 November 1793

| Lot | | gns |
|---|---|---|
| 8 | SHORT TAIL, by Shakespeare. This cow was lot 18 in the late Mr Fowler's sale. | 38 |
| 9 | EYEBRIGHT, by a bull bred by Mr Varnam | 51 |
| 14 | STRAWBERRY, by a Dishley bull | 31 |
| 16 | BRINDLED EYEBRIGHT | 33 |
| 26 | PENN, Dam by a son of the Hampshire Bull. | 35 |
| 27 | GREG, Dam by a Dishley Bull | 15 |
| 28 | NANCY, Dam by a son of the Hampshire Bull | 20 |
| 29 | YOUNG DANDY | 30 |
| 30 | BRINDLED FINCH TIDY | 29 |
| 31 | YOUNG LOVELY | 20 |
| 33 | YOUNG EYEBRIGHT – Dam by a Son of The Hampshire Bull | |

Bulls and Bull Calves

| | | |
|---|---|---|
| 34 | SHAKESPEARE (bred by the late Mr Fowler) by Shakespeare, off Young Nell. Whoever buys this lot, the seller makes it a condition that he shall have the privilege of having 2 cows bulled by him yearly. | 400 |
| 35 | Bull-calf by lot 34 | 23 |
| 37 | ,,    ,,   ,,   ,,   34 | 31 |
| 38 | ,,    ,,   ,,   ,,   34 | 31 |

Second Day's Sale

| | | |
|---|---|---|
| 45 | One 3 yrs heifer (Bought by Lord Harborough) | 70 |
| 47 | ,, ,, ,, ,, | 32 |
| 48 | ,, ,, ,, ,, | 35 |
| 52 | ,, ,, ,, ,, | 35 |
| 55 | One 2 yrs heifer | 25 |
| 57 | ,, ,, ,, ,, | 60 |
| 58 | ,, ,, ,, ,, | 84 |
| 60 | ,, ,, ,, ,, | 29 |
| 61 | ,, ,, ,, ,, | 25 |
| 64 | ,, ,, ,, ,, | 27 |

Shakespeare, Lot 34, was bought by a partnership from Leicestershire and afterwards served cows at 25 guineas each. Pitt saw him in use at Mr Stone's of Quorndon. All the heifers offered at the sale were by Lot 34 and, together with the cows, had been bulled by him, except for Lot 52 which had been bulled by a son of Garrick. Five four-year-old bullocks, perfectly quiet for work plus their working harness, made 11 guineas each. The 64 lots of Longhorns averaged £31 15s 3d, but unless they were by Shakespeare they made low figures.

Paget was also an 'ardent and successful' breeder of New Leicester sheep and an associate of Robert Bakewell's. Paget sold his flock at the same time as his Longhorns, on 16 November 1793. The top sheep made 62, 52 and 45 guineas – prices still within the range of comprehension of sheep farmers over 200 years later. Overall, 130 females, including 20 shearlings, averaged £25 16s 11d each and grossed £3,200, an enormous sum at the time.

## Mr Thomas Prinsep of Croxall

Pitt, in his *Agricultural Report of Derbyshire*, of 20 May 1794, said:

I viewed the stock of Mr Thomas Prinsep of Croxall [on the Staffordshire/Derbyshire border] and I shall just observe that they are of the Longhorn breed and, by long attention, have been brought to a high degree of superiority. Large, thick, heavy and well made, with a pretty good show for milking, and such a disposition to fatten, that Mr Prinsep observes the young stock are obliged to be almost starved by short pasturage; otherwise

The bull Bright and a cow, the property of T. Prinsep in 1794.

they make fat and never stand the bull. Cows give an average of about eight quarts of milk each which their owner thinks equal, from its superior quality, to a much greater quantity from inferior breeds. Mr Prinsep's bull named Bright, which always has been and invariably will be, kept for his own stock, is a majestic, noble animal. Large, heavy in the valuable parts, with the least imaginable proportions of offal, with a skin handling soft and sleek. This animal is so gentle and docile that three or four persons may handle him without the least signs of ferocity, or even notice, on his part. Brighteye, the son of Bright, now three years old is a most beautiful and complete animal.

Marshall, writing in 1784, informed us that Bright was by Shakespeare and therefore of the celebrated Twopenny line.

Twelve years later another authority visiting Mr Prinsep said that the dairy of milking cows were all in such high condition that they were really fit for the butcher, and that a seven-year-old cow, which was killed, turned the scales at 104 stone.

In 1784 Marshall said that a German prince was probably less respected in the environs of his residence that Mr Prinsep in the neighbourhood of Croxall. On a later visit, Marshall wrote that, 'Although the cows of his breeding were of very fine quality in the past, his present herd show evident marks of improvement. Every cow and heifer of the Shakespeare blood is recognisable by sight, by the extreme fineness of the fore-end, the width of the hips, and the formation of the rump.'

Prinsep had hired Shakespeare from Mr Fowler for the amazing sum of 80 guineas per season for two seasons. Prinsep's foundation cow, also by the name of Bright, had been purchased from a Mr Chadwick of Castle Bromwich, and was by Webster's bull Bloxedge. The Prinsep herd was sold on 25–26 September 1811 at Croxall, Derbyshire, the sale conducted by Mr Boot. The 65 head of cattle averaged 61 guineas each, the principal prices being:

| | Bulls | |
|---|---|---|
| Roscins | 6 years | 85 guineas |
| R | 4 | 125 |
| D | 4 | 100 |
| L | 3 | 105 |
| A | 1 | 130 |

| Cows | | |
|---|---|---|
| Dumpling | 4 years | 42 guineas |
| Mottled Rumps | 4 | 42 |
| Comely Lupin | 6 | 64 |
| Doll | 5 | 78 |
| Lonk-Horn Lupin | 5 | 42 |
| Mottle-back Lupin | 6 | 200 |
| White Lupin | 7 | 220 |
| Yellow Lupin | 8 | 125 |
| Beauty | 6 | 200 |
| Lonk | 8 | 45 |
| Dowdy | 7 | 80 |
| Dishley Rumps | 4 | 45 |
| Cherry | 8 | 43 |
| Dishley Cherry | 6 | 48 |
| Dishley Daisy | 7 | 68 |
| Tidy | 6 | 70 |

| Heifers | | |
|---|---|---|
| Mottle Back Lupin II | 3 years | 58 guineas |
| Rumps | 3 | 47 |
| Yellow Lupin II | 3 | 92 |
| Dumpling | 3 | 90 |
| Lupin | 3 | 60 |
| Cherry II | 3 | 90 |
| White Lupin II | 2 | 80 |
| Strawberry | 2 | 50 |
| Lonk II | 2 | 40 |
| Brindy | 2 | 50 |
| Beauty II | 1 | 34 |
| Lonk III | 1 | 40 |
| Cherry III | 1 | 35 |
| Brind | 1 | 30 |
| Strawberry II | 1 | 35 |
| Nell | 1 | 60 |

Bull calves: 11 bull calves under six months made prices of
30, 34, 55, 60, 37, 160, 32, 75, 32 and 45 guineas
respectively.

Prinsep's grandson, Mr T. Levett Prinsep, reverted back to
Longhorns in 1873 when he purchased foundation animals for his
herd at Mr Chapman's sale. He went on to preside over the

meeting held at Birmingham Fatstock Show in 1876 to establish a
Longhorn Herd Society and Herd Book.

## Richard Astley of Odstone Hall

Mr Richard Astley of Odstone Hall, Market Bosworth, Leicestershire, was another noted breeder in the early years of the breed's
zenith. He was a large exporter of Longhorns to Ireland, where
several of his bulls were held in very high regard.

His fame was mainly based on being the owner of a celebrated
cow which was exhibited all over the country, being transported
by horse-drawn van. She must have been an exceptional animal
and it is unfortunate that her pedigree, with those of the rest of
Astley's cattle, has not survived.

Other than the fact that he was a large buyer at the Rollright
sale in 1791, and therefore dipped deeply in the Shakespeare
blood, no other records of how his herd was bred have been
found. Thomas and William Knowles, his neighbours, were
partners with him in the Rollright purchases.

Astley was a member of the Dishley Society from its formative
years, although he later fell foul of its rules and was ejected. He
was also one of the founder members of the Smithfield Club,
being at the inaugural meeting in London, in December 1798.

In 1797, Washington, a bull, and Lady Washington, the bull's
dam, both from Rollright, were in his possession but pensioned
off. He kept a dairy of 30 Longhorn milking cows, which were
the largest and best, except for those of Mr Prinsep, that William
Pitt, the agricultural author, had ever seen.

Richard Astley's farm consisted of 500 acres and belonged to his
brother, Dugdale Astley, of Everly, Wiltshire. Pitt declared the
farm to be 'very productive, Richard having removed the ant hills
from his pastures, and levelled the surface of his meadowland, by
removing uncouth ill-formed banks, taking care to preserve the
top soil in its proper place.' One wonders if this work was carried
out after Astley had seen such procedures at Dishley.

Following the passing of the legendary breeders – Webster,
Bakewell, Fowler, Prinsep and their fellows – the Longhorn

rapidly declined. Their empire began to crumble and decay, not totally from the onslaught of the up and coming Shorthorn but rather from within their own walls. By 1815 their battle was all but lost and the 'Druid' (H. H. Dixon) came very close to the truth when he wrote in 1815: 'When the Durham Ox (Shorthorn) began his six years of caravan (exhibition) life the fate of the Longhorn was sealed.'

During the years when the Longhorn fell from favour, it could quite easily have slipped out of existence, but it still held captive a few faithful hearts who, having seen the mistakes of their predecessors, endeavoured to do better for their chosen breed. Biding their time, they waited for the breed's re-emergence to popularity in the mid-19th century. The ancient fame and glory of the Longhorn was once more to cast its spell over many of those who had deserted it. The 'Leicester Curly Coats' were again remembered for their hardy constitution and ability to thrive on poor pasture. The light of former days was beginning to shine once more, and from sales such as Mr Chapman's of Upton in 1873, many new herds were to spring to life. The second age of the Longhorn had come.

# CHAPTER NINE

# The Chapman Family of Nuneaton

> There is something very quaint and grand in a field full of
> Longhorns and Mr Chapman's grand old bull, the Earl of
> Derby, with 32 milking cows around him in the great
> meadow was a sight ever to be remembered by all admirers
> of livestock.
>
> (*The Druid – H. H. Dixon*)

One of the oldest herds of Longhorns on record was the Upton herd, maintained by the Chapman family near Nuneaton for 117 years. A George Chapman went to live at Upton in 1745 and started buying Longhorn cows in 1756. He hired bulls, first from Robert Bakewell and later from Robert Fowler of Little Rollright in Oxfordshire. The last bull he ever hired was Bakewell's noted Twopenny, afterwards using his own home-bred sires. He acquired the reputation of being a breeder of sound judgement and Bakewell once said of him: 'George Chapman has one of the best herds of Longhorns that I know anywhere.'

On the death of George Chapman in 1802, the herd was taken over by his son, Samuel, and later by his grandson, Richard Hemming Chapman. They continued to cultivate their herd's usefulness for dairy purposes, for which it was famed. The name of R. H. Chapman became well known in the show ring, the herd having many successes over a period of 30 years. Calke Abbey records reveal that: 'Mr Chapman on three occasions in the past few years won the laurels from the Shorthorns, although the animals have been bred mainly for dairy and cheese-making purposes, and not for exhibition especially.'

In 1850, Mr Chapman's bull Marquis of Exeter took the first prize of £20 at the Royal Agricultural Society Show, held at Exeter. In 1851, the same bull took the prize of £10 at the Royal Show held at Windsor, and at Birmingham in 1853 he took £20 and a silver medal.

When Chapman exhibited his five-year-old bull Old Sparkenhoe at the Plymouth Royal Show in 1865, he collected the first prize of 15 guineas. The men of the west were reported to show how impressed they had been with the Marquis of Exeter 15 years before, by exclaiming that Sparkenhoe was the same bull – thus suggesting how true to type both bulls must have been, as well as how vividly the illustrious stranger of earlier years was remembered. At the later show, Old Sparkenhoe was considered a great curiosity and became the main attraction in the cattle lines for sightseers. Many people in that area had not before seen Longhorns and it was wondered what bovine tribe the bull could belong to. A reporter, giving an account of the stock classes for the day, said that 'Not one person in 500 could guess his breed.' The catalogue for the show states that Sparkenhoe's sire was Tom, bred by Col. Inge, a Longhorn breeder of great note in Staffordshire, and his dam was Fillpail, also a prize cow at the Royal and bred by

*Sparkenhoe, bred by Colonel Inge in 1860 and winner at the RASE in 1865.*

Mrs Baker of Little Rollright, Oxfordshire, where the great Long-horn breeder Fowler previously lived.

R. H. Chapman was one of the founder members of the Longhorn Cattle Society in 1876, even though he had, after great deliberation, retired in 1873, and a sale had been called for 16 December of that year. The event was extremely well attended, with one estimate being that 600 were present. Amongst the distinguished company were Lord Howe (the landed proprietor of the district), Mr Heygate, MP, Mr T. Cox, Mr Pickering (agent for Lord Bagot), Mr Bosworth (agent for Sir John Crewe), Mr T. Nichols (agent for Mr T. Prinsep), Mr J. Burbery, and Mr Hanson Sale of Atherstone.

The tables for luncheon were set in double lines in an outbuilding amidst a profusion of banners and evergreens. The pillars and roof timbers were decorated with the heads or skulls and polished horns of prize-winning specimens of the Longhorn breed. On the walls were hung many oil paintings of past favourites, amongst the most outstanding being Shakespeare, the brindled bull, which made 400 guineas in 1793 at Mr Paget's sale. The picture was the property of Mr T. Paget of Humberstone at the time and had been loaned for the occasion.

Hanging near to Shakespeare, and looking very like him, was a portrait of Mr Fowler's Brindled Beauty, lent by Mr Warner, this cow having made £273 at the Rollright sale in 1791. Then, by way of contrast in depth of carcase and colour, was an oil painting of a pair of Mr Warner's red-sided white cows. There was a portrait of a cow bred by Mr T. Prinsep, with horns curling up several feet in advance of her head, and two other pictures showing specimens of the Croxall herd which was dispersed in 1811 when prices were very high.

It was noted by onlookers that if these paintings were true likenesses of their subjects, then the Longhorns of Mr Chapman's breeding had made great strides since that time. The comment was made that the breed was much improved in a hundred years and that Shakespeare and Brindled Beauty of former days were no more to be compared with the Lady Calke or Lady Rollright of the later age than 'chalk is like cheese'.

An exact likeness, again in oils, was on display of Mr Chapman's Old Sparkenhoe bull which won first prize at the 1865 Royal

*This steer was bred and fed by R. H. Chapman, who considered him one of the best of the breed ever exhibited. In 1863 he won £25 and two silver medals. He was sold to the butcher at three years eight months for 50 guineas.*

Show at Plymouth. Another very striking canvas portrayed the Upton herd's Marquis of Exeter, which first appeared at the Royal Show at Exeter in 1850. In 1862 and 1863, Mr Chapman won first prizes at London and Birmingham with oxen which were both shown to perfection on one canvas, displaying proportions that were firm evidence for the assertion that one of them was the best Longhorn ever exhibited up to that date.

Lord Howe occupied the chair for the proceedings and, reflecting the interest shown in the event, letters of apology, regretting inability to attend, were received from Lord Leigh, Mr C. N. Newdegate, MP, Mr A. Pell, MP, the Marquis of Queensberry, Lord Westmeath, Sir John Crewe and others.

Mr Heygate, MP, proposing the toast to 'The breeders of Longhorns', said that 'All in attendance that day would regret the breaking up of this noble herd which has become so famous in history.'

Lord Howe, proposing the main toast of the morning, 'Success to Mr Chapman', said he did so with mingled feelings of regret and satisfaction – satisfaction in having to uphold the reputation of one who through life had proved himself a straightforward and honest neighbour, and regret at the loss of one who had endeared himself to them by so many manly qualities. He was perfectly certain that there was not a soul within ten miles of Upton who would not vouch for the intense interest and enthusiasm he had thrown into everything he took in hand. He regretted his loss from the neighbourhood very much, and he wished him all the success in his future undertakings that an honest man deserved. The herd had descended from father to son for several generations and, while he regretted the loss the neighbourhood would sustain through Mr Chapman's retirement, he wished him all the success, prosperity and usefulness that could attend him.

Mr Chapman, who responded with considerable feeling, said the present position was forced on him after very serious consideration. He had had many thoughtful days and sleepless nights in coming to the conclusion he had arrived at, and though he had to take that public occasion in expressing his obligations to his landlord, who had even allowed him to choose his successor, he took the liberty of saying that farming was not what it was. He said that some of his friends had asked how he could break up the home and herd of his ancestors? His reply was that labour was now a most serious item in expenditure, making cheese

*Earl of Upton 7th, calved March 1872 and bred by R. H. Chapman.*

production more difficult and less profitable. He praised the men who worked for him as being a well-conducted and skilful body of men, but past middle age, and it was in vain that he looked for the new generation that was to take their place. He said it was his intention to retain all the young stock and so would not be losing his links with the breed entirely, when he retired to St Asaph in Wales.

Mr J. H. Burbery gave an address which was very sound. 'Do not starve your animals, but do not pamper them; give them good, wholesome food, with plenty of fresh air and water; keep them not too closely housed but let their natural hair protect them; and then you will find, as I have done, that for general purposes no breed will beat the Longhorn.'

The Upton herd had, since its foundation in 1756, been carefully bred from the best strains of blood that could be procured. It rightly took its place as one of the oldest and best herds in existence. Many people went to the sale as first-time purchasers looking to lay foundations of future herds. It is well known that similarity of characteristics in cattle always denote purity of race, and careful selection of a recognised type during a long period is the only way to secure this greatly desired effect. Like the Drakelow Baronet, the Chapman family succeeded in breeding 'a dairy of Longhorn cows, alike in colour and shape'. The 51 offered at the Upton sale were reported to have shown a remarkable likeness to one another. The herd was bred for its good milking qualities and for the use of the milk in cheese-making.★ The animals for the sale were therefore in lean working condition, being worked harder than many other herds.

The sale then proceeded with the top price of 50 guineas going to the two-year-old prize-winning heifer, Lady Calke. The sale

★A few years before the dispersal of the Chapman herd, a contest was held with a friend, a Mr S. Craven Pilgrim, a Shorthorn breeder, whose animals hailed from the famous Bates blood, and were cultivated for their milking properties. At the height of the summer grass in June, both men selected six of their best cows. The Shorthorns produced 152 lb of milk against the Longhorns' 135 lb, but the weight of curd for the Longhorns was 19½ lb as against 14½ lb for the Shorthorns. The trial was repeated again in September of the same year, the whole of Mr Pilgrim's cows, numbering 36, against 32 of Mr Chapman's Longhorns. The Shorthorns produced 605 lb of milk, making 66½ lb of curd. The Longhorns produced 553 lb of milk, making 69 lb of curd.

was conducted by Messrs Lythall and Clarke and the following prices were obtained:

| Lot | | Guineas | Purchaser |
|---|---|---|---|
| 1 | Canley | 29 | Lord Bagot |
| 2 | Dairy Maid | 27 | Lord Bagot |
| 3 | Light of Other Days | 30 | Mr Parker |
| 4 | Oxford | 24 | Mr J. H. Burbery |
| 5 | Pallas, 4 years | 44 | W. T. Cox, Spondon Hall |
| 6 | Milkmaid | 23 | W. T. Cox |
| 7 | Moss Rose | 24 | Lord Bagot |
| 8 | Tulip | 20 | Mr J. H. Clay |
| 9 | Duchess | 23 | W. T. Cox |
| 10 | Kenilworth | 29 | Mr Shaw |
| 11 | Brindled Beauty | 36 | Sir John H. Crewe |
| 12 | Lady Calke, 2 years | 50 | Mr Parker |
| 13 | Upton, 2 years | 40 | Mr J. H. Burbery |
| 14 | Young Croperdy, 2 years | 38 | Mr Forrest, Kenilworth |
| 15 | Rose | 38 | W. T. Cox |
| 16 | Lady Stowe | 36½ | R. Warner |
| 17 | Young Dairymaid | 42 | Sir John H. Crewe |
| 18 | Young Fillpail | 35 | Mr T. Levett Prinsep |
| 19 | Ivanhoe | 28 | W. T. Cox |
| 20 | Nancy | 40 | W. T. Cox |
| 21 | Brailsford | 35 | Mr T. L. Prinsep |
| 22 | Lady Westmorland | 30 | Lord Bagot |
| 23 | Young Dishley | 25 | Lord Bagot |
| 24 | Cumberland Duchess | 42 | Sir John H. Crewe |
| 25 | Farewell | 36 | Mr Forrest |
| 26 | Croxall, 2 years | 45 | Sir John H. Crewe |
| 27 | Spondon | 36 | Mr Forrest |
| 28 | Fradley | 25 | Mr Shaw |
| 29 | Willscote | 27 | Mr Ball, Measham |
| 30 | Nellie | 26 | Mr Foster |
| 31 | Satchwell | 25 | Mr Foster |
| 32 | Countess | 22 | Mr Clarke |
| 33 | Fillpail | 29½ | Mr Degg |
| 34 | Sparkenhoe | 24½ | Mr Fox |
| 35 | Brailsford | 29 | W. T. Cox |
| 36 | Wry Neck | 25 | W. T. Cox |
| 37 | Cherry | 30 | Mr Clarke |

| 38 | Blossom | 27½ | Mr Clarke |
|---|---|---|---|
| 39 | Dishley | 29 (fat cow) | |
| 40 | Milker | 25 (fat cow) | |
| 41 | Croperdy | 42 | Sir John H. Crewe |
| 42 | Buttercup | 22½ (fat cow) | |
| 43 | Woodcote | 28 (fat cow) | |
| 44 | Hagley | 30 | Mr Shaw |
| 45 | Banbury | 28 | Mr Shaw |
| 46 | Lilly | 27 (fat cow) | |
| 47 | Sally Dick | 27 (fat cow) | |
| 48 | Ivanhoe | 30 (fat cow) | |
| 49 | Lady Rollright | 46½ | Mr Fox |
| | (prize heifer at Birmingham) | | |

## Bulls

Twopenny, 3 years, bred by Mr J. C. Moore, sire of Mr Godfrey's
Sampson                                29 gns                  Lord Bagot
Old Time, 1 year, bred by Mr Hewertson, Westmorland.
                                       40 gns                  Sir John H. Crewe

*Total of sale*                 1,600 guineas
*Average of 51 cows and bulls*  £32 18s 10d

The yearlings and calves were reserved and subsequently sold as two-year-olds during the Birmingham Show weeks in 1874 and 1875. In 1874, the 12 heifers reached an average of nearly £37 and Brindled Beauty, the star lot and said by Mr J. Neville Fitt to be one of the most beautiful heifers he had ever seen, was knocked down to Mr Townley-Parker at £67 4s. In 1875, 15 very even heifers and in better condition than those of the year before, but with no Brindled Beauty to outshine the rest, averaged £34 15s with the top price of £49 7s being for Uplands Last Link.

Considering the smaller number of Longhorn buyers at this period, these prices compared very favourably with the large number of Shorthorn sales held during that time. The 78 head of cattle which Mr Chapman sold over a two-year period averaged £34 to total £2,700. And he still retained a few heifers to breed from in his retirement.

# CHAPTER TEN

# The Revivalists

The Longhorn may now be said to have become something
of a fancy beast in England.

*(Sporting Gazette, 1874)*

Any livestock breeder would testify to the pleasure gained from
viewing a fellow-breeder's stock, be it on their home ground,
or at a show or sale. This phenomenon is not restricted to our own
time, but it is one which has taken place since men first kept
animals. During the 19th century, when the Longhorn had taken a
great dive in popularity, its cause was championed by a few brave
men who were willing, and admittedly able, in monetary terms, to
fly in the face of popularity and carry on with the breed of their
forefathers.

Wonderful records of herd visits have come down to us from
this period, courtesy of some excellent articles in publications such
as the *Sporting Gazette* and *Bell's Weekly Messenger*. Even then it
was a rarity for a Longhorn herd to feature in their pages. It is
therefore a very special privilege to join with these gentlemen on
their expeditions, to those hallowed grounds, and to be given our
own guided tour of herds which existed so many years ago.

## Mr R. Brown of the Old Manor House, Farewell

The breeders of this old established [the Longhorn] sort will
probably be found mustered in force at Farewell near Lichfield
on Wednesday, 15 March 1876, when a herd bred with the
greatest care for purity of pedigree and great milking qualities,

the property of Mr R. Brown, whose health compels him to relinquish business, will be offered for sale. The herd came into the possession of the present family through Mr J. L. Brown in 1807 and was founded at an earlier date than that, the farm having been in the hands of the family for 300 years. The late Mr J. L. Brown was a successful exhibitor for many years and a winner of no less than ten cups at the Royal and local shows, and amongst the animals now offered will be found the hardy constitution and other valuable qualities for which this breed of cattle is especially prized. Space will not allow us to give a list of the bulls that have been of service at Farewell during the century but we may say that the most noted of their day are, with exceptions, to be found in the list of sires there used, and, amongst their breeders are to be found the names of Meek; Robinson of Coton; Prinsep of Croxall; Ward of Tixall; Astley of Odstone; Smith of Snitterfield; Salisbury of Dordon; Shaw of Fradley Old Hall, near Lichfield; Chapman of Upton; Burbery of Kenilworth; Warner of Weston; and Twycross of Canley. In 1841, Mr Brown's father sold to the Hon. W. B. Nugent of Higham Grange near Hinkley, six Longhorns which averaged £82 8s 2d, amongst them being the Shakespeare bull, £127, and the Cherry cow, £100. The herd has for many years been bred entirely for milk production rather than show.

The herd having been in the possession of Mr R. Brown or his family for 70 years, most of the principal names in the Longhorn world were present or represented at the sale. The prices achieved were not so high as at Mr Chapman's sale (see pp. 96ff), perhaps because the herd had not recently been bred for the show ring, or for the characteristic finching or white mark on the back which is much sought after today. Dairy qualities were of greater import-ance to him than colour, and a bystander at the sale gave witness to the superior fleshing qualities of the animals: 'While their milk was so good, the cheese made from it was vastly superior to ordinary cheese.' Cows made up to 26 guineas, heifers to 24 guineas and calves to 10 guineas. Purchases at the sale included the bull Nelson to Mr W. T. Cox for £35 10s; the bull General to Sir John Crewe; and the heifer, Lady Prinsep to Mr T. L. Prinsep for £25 4s. Cows averaged £20 each, but were only in store condition.

Mr Brown had used a bull called Washington by Mr Meek's

Washington out of Prinsep's Brindled Beauty from 1808 to 1812.

Brown won seven £10 silver cups and three £5 cups at the old Staffordshire General Agricultural Society Shows at Lichfield, when competing against Herefords, Shorthorns and Devons, often with 20 entries per class, from 1813 to 1820. Prizes were also taken at the Royal Shows at Derby and Shrewsbury.

A friend of Mr J. Neville Fitt's attended the sale and reported to him:

> The great revival in favour of what is now called the old Staffordshire Longhorn induced me to go and see a herd sold on its native soil. The morning, like all the rest in this month of March, was a truly cold and wet one; however, I resolved to make the best of it and, after admiring the lovely cathedral of Lichfield, went on my way to Farewell; on the road I was joined by a working man and we soon got into conversation about the stock to be sold. He said that Mr Brown's were the only beasts of the sort about, and when pressed for the reason of this difference in farmers' tastes, added: 'Why the people here know nothing about them, they all run after the new fashioned sort, but Mr Brown has tried them and knows they are best for him.' Being questioned as to the reason why they were better, he said: 'Why, they give such good and rich milk, that the cheese made from them is as much different as between chalk and cheese, and they are such good feeding stock, and are not gluttons at eating, but will eat anything you give them and, what is more, they will do on poor land, and this Mr Brown has found out many years ago. I have seen them for years and know it is quite true.' I think this is a good character reference of the breed, spoken without any interest to serve, and after a real honest Staffordshire fashion.

## The Calke Abbey Estate

In the south Derbyshire village of Ticknall lie the gates to the park which surrounds Calke Abbey, the seat of the Harpur-Crewe family since 1622. The history of Calke can be traced back to the 12th century when it was selected by Augustinian monks as the site for a priory but it did not come into its present name of Abbey until 1808. It is now owned by the National Trust.

The two members of the family of interest in the history of

Longhorns are Sir George Crewe, who came into his inheritance in 1819, and his son, Sir John, who succeeded him in 1844.

Sir George took his responsibilities as 8th baronet, and one of the largest landowners in the country, most seriously and devoted his time, as steward of the family estates, to the welfare of his tenants and lands. He brought about great improvements, both to the land and to the conditions in which his tenants had to live. That was something which had been ignored by the generations who had gone before him, their main interests being of a sporting nature.

Sir George was living at a time when gentlemen had become keen enthusiasts of agriculture, their imaginations fired by the great improvers who had gone before. Sir George had a genuine admiration for Robert Bakewell and his Longhorn cattle and collected as much information and as many mementoes as he could gather on the great man. He also built up a large and very fine herd of Longhorn cattle. Although his improvements were largely confined to the outdoors, Sir George purchased some remarkable paintings, including some by John Ferneley, the Leicestershire horse artist. Also amongst the collection is a fine painting of a Longhorn bull at Dishley Grange by John Boultbee, Boultbee being the only artist known to have painted Bakewell himself. Sir George carried on with Longhorns for a good many years, until they finally gave way to the breed very much at its zenith, the Shorthorn.

Sir George died at the age of 48 in 1844, honoured and beloved by all who knew him. He was thereafter dubbed the 'Honourable Baronet'. As the great mantle passed from father to son, the passion for agriculture remained undiminished. Sir John Harpur-Crewe shunned public life and duties and spent most of his time on his estate at Calke. In 1860 he reinstated Longhorns there, founding his herd on the best strains that could be obtained. They, together with the Portland sheep which had been introduced into the park by his great-grandfather, Sir Henry, became his great passions in life. Like his father before him he was a great admirer of Bakewell and, in championing Bakewell's breed of cattle, he gave powerful assistance in preventing the pure-bred race from slipping quietly into extinction.

At this time it was common policy amongst the farming fraternity to cross Longhorn cows with a Shorthorn bull to obtain an excellent dairy animal, beloved of the small farmer. The first crosses were said to be very hardy cattle, fattening quickly. But their calves were considered uncertain and in the majority of instances the third- or fourth-generation animals, crossed back to the Longhorn, were considered to be Longhorns but did not have the good qualities of the original stock. They were smaller animals, poor milkers, poor fatteners and were not always certain to hold to the bull. It was claimed that a third of these crosses proved infertile.

Having arrived at this sad situation, many breeders wished they had kept with the original Longhorns. But good Longhorn bulls were almost impossible to obtain at that time. Sir John, like men before him, found the Longhorn too beautiful and useful to be allowed to fade away forever. It is our good fortune that he had the courage to follow his own convictions and not the path to the Shorthorn, which was so popular at the time. He also left us a unique legacy of records at Calke Abbey.

## Sir John Harpur-Crewe and his Longhorns

On 21 February 1874, the *Sporting Gazette* published the following article on 'Sir John Harpur-Crewe's Longhorns'. A copy of the article has been preserved at Calke Abbey.

> The Longhorn may now be said to have become something of a fancy beast in England. Gradually ousted from his position on the broad Midland pastures by the quicker feeding, and therefore better paying, Shorthorn, he has retired from the homestead of the tenant to the foldyard of the landlord where in a few instances his picturesque appearance has caused him to hold his ground against the Oxfords and the Duchesses (well-known families of Shorthorn cattle). True, some tenants still stick to the old sort but the lover of Longhorns, when he looks around and enumerates the few holdings on which they are yet to be found in Leicestershire, Derbyshire, Lancashire or Westmorland, and then reverts to the times when nearly all those grazing districts owned their sway, may well say, indeed, 'The old order changeth for the new.' They bear the character of a very old and original race about them and, perhaps, with the exception of the

Highlanders and Welsh cattle, approach nearer in appearance to the wild types than any breed that still remains amongst us. Their long horns, some drooping in long forward curves by the side of their cheeks, others standing out in graceful turns or, as they are occasionally seen, standing almost straight out at right angles to the head and hoisted like those of an antelope, combined with their rough, shaggy coats which hang in winter time, at any rate, like manes on their forequarters, and are especially thick on the foreheads, give them certainly a most weird appearance. The colour also, generally brindled and ranging from almost black to dull brown or dun on the sides, becoming mottled as it approaches the back, belly and quarters which, for the most part are white, certainly detracts nothing from the idea that they must come of a wild and ancient race, and in looking at the bulls we can well fancy that it was one of the kind who had taken a mad freak in his head, that the sturdy old Baron saw chased by the butchers and their dogs at Stamford, and forthwith instituted the once-fashionable sport of bull baiting. Might they not well recall the poet's description of bovine duel in old times –

> The stooping warriors, aiming head to head,
> Engage their clashing horns. With dreadful sound
> The forest rattles, and the rocks rebound.
> They fence, they push, and pushing loudly roar;
> Their dewlaps and their sides are bathed in gore.

Their history, however, rests in private hands, as there is no *Herd Book*, and they have received but little encouragement, as compared with other breeds, at shows either of fat or breeding stock. Nevertheless, when brought into direct competition with others, they have held their own very fairly and, in some instances, taken prizes over the heads of Shorthorns and other more favoured kinds.

Having been granted permission to see the herd of Sir John Harpur-Crewe at Calke Abbey, we not long ago made a pilgrimage into Derbyshire for that purpose.

Although early in February, mild and balmy as the May morning of the poets, or the day that first lures the flyfisher to the stream, was the day on which we found ourselves on the road to Calke. What a pretty drive it was over the four miles that separates the quiet little town of Ashby-de-le-Zouch from the Abbey! Unfortunately, beautiful as was the weather, there was a thin haze in the air which just served to shut out distant objects and confine the view within a distance of a mile or two, so that the most inveterate day-dreamer would have been puzzled to fix in his mind the spot most suitable for the renowned lists, or settle the route by which Rowena started on her homeward journey to the Saxon Grange. Worse still, it shut from view the bold range of hills known as Charnwood Forest where, long years ago, we have enjoyed, in our 'youth's first prime', sport with the Quorn which, if it wanted the steeple-chasing attractions of the other side of the [river] Wreake, was not wanting in either interest or pleasure. However, our blood is tamed now, and we look at the surrounding country more with a view to its stock-carrying capabilities than its likelihood for holding a scent, and descant more on the value per acre than on the practicability of the fences. So, as we pass the little village of Smisby, where Sir John's boundary commences, we are content to learn that the land is good and forward, bearing heavy crops of hay. As the park is neared we come on a lot of thriving Scotch beasts, which the mildness of the season still allowed to be foddered in the open field, and then beyond the stone wall we enter the park, and almost at once find ourselves driving through a magnificent herd of deer. Right well they look, too, though the park is somewhat heavily stocked and our guide and charioteer points with pride to a big buck lying down amongst some rushes, with a magnificent 'head', whose turn it will be to die when the season comes round once more, while another just beyond him is scarcely inferior in any way and will most likely both hear and feel the crack of doom from the rifle ere the summer is over. Much as we admire them, however, we must not linger amongst the deer, for Mr Bosworth, the steward, is already on the lookout to conduct us to the farm where the dairyman is waiting with his pets all in order for inspection. We must just linger, however, as we go, to note the peacocks, turkeys, guinea fowls and Dorkings whose name is legion and whose abode is at the snug steading where the cows are provided for. Anything neater or more commodious than the accommodation here is seldom seen. Each cow is stalled well, bedded down, and honoured with a small board on which her name is painted, hung over her head, while behind them there is a broad passage, wider than is found in many stables; and, as regards freedom from offensive smells and general cleanliness, the most fastidious stud groom need not be ashamed to compare notes with this well kept cow byre, which is light and airy, yet warm.

First in honour, as perchance in quality, came Tulip III by a bull named Thorpe out of Tulip, who carried off the only prize offered in which she could compete both at Birmingham and London in 1868, and for whom a butcher was ready to give the high price of 60 gns. Sir John, however, preferred to bring her home and she is now certainly one of the finest cows in the herd and has since bred him four calves, though a certain amount of patchiness about the rump still remains to tell of her training days. A right good looking cow she is now and one that any man might be proud to own. Next to her stands Brindle III by Dairyman (a bull, I believe of Sir John's breeding) out of Brindle, a nice level cow and a good specimen of her kind. Lovely IV, somewhat older, is a big cow by Young Sampson out of Lovely III, and Beauty III, with her wide spreading horns and lengthy frame carried one back more into the old fashioned type. Fanny, sixth of the name, is reported as being of a first rate family; and Trimmer II, light coloured though she be, with her fine barrel and bowed horn, is considered a rare specimen of the sort. Tulip IV keeps well up to the prestige of that family and the dark brindled Upton is a grand beast; while Bright Eye drops back to

*Sir John Crewe's favourite cow, Tulip, who took first prizes at both Birmingham and London in 1868 and for whom a butcher offered the high price of 60 guineas. Sir John, however, declined the offer and took her home to Calke, where she went on to found the outstanding Tulip tribe.*

the old Lancashire sort. Brindle II, a good coloured cow, would probably ere now have committed 'the happy despatch' if left in a state of nature but civilisation has stepped in and prevented her horns, by the aid of the knife, from growing right through her head, as they inevitably must have done. Canley II is well worthy of the name she bears, and Joan III does no discredit to her family history. Leaving her, we come on yet a younger Tulip, good as the rest of the name.

In the next shed we find Snowdrop, the sole remaining memento of Sir John's Shorthorn fancy and we can well appreciate the fiât which reserved her when the rest were sold. Next to her is Titney, a good thick beast, and somewhat of a curiosity, as she has one horn growing up and the other down. The next worthy of mention are Daisy and an unnamed companion, both of the real, rough-looking Longhorn character and bought on account of the sort. We then come on a nice two-year-old out of Tulip, a black or nearly black and white (somewhat an unusual colour). On then to Brindle, and Patty, a heifer for whose good looks we cannot say a great deal, and so ends the home-bred ones.

There were yet, however, half a dozen purchased at Mr Chapman's sale to see, and right good ones they were, full of that mysterious thing called quality, whatever it may be, but scarcely of the size or weight, notwithstanding more flesh, of the home-bred ones. However, Young Dairymaid, Crossredy (who has strangely wide open horns), Dishley, Brindled Beauty, Cumberland Duchess and Croxall cannot fail to improve any herd they enter, and will no doubt do good service to the one which, as was recently shown in the columns of *The Gazette*, they have been implanted. We think we are correct in stating the present strength of the herd to be 41, not counting the young stock yet to calve or the bulls.

Our next visit was to Old Time, the yearling bought in the autumn at Mr Chapman's sale, who has both grown and improved since he came to Calke, and promises to make a valuable bull. He has a rare head and horn, is a good colour and is a nice level young beast, being bred in Westmorland by Mr Matthew Hewertson and got by Tom Boy out of Daisy. He was bought by Sir John principally, we believe, with the view of introducing fresh blood into the herd. There is another young one of the same age by the prize bull Sampson who promises well and has an exceeding well-sprung rib and capital quarters, though his colour, being much lighter, we fancy somewhat detracts from his appearance. A nice young bull calf completed our inspection of this side of the yard and then we went away by the neat poultry houses in one of which, by the way, a sea eagle has held solitary state for upwards of twenty years, whose screams at strangers are a better warning of intrusion than even a dog. He is said to have got loose once but was captured again ere he had played the havoc amongst his feathered neighbours that might reasonably have been anticipated.

Beyond him we came on a fine two-year-old bull by Earl of Upton out of Joan, now promoted to the post of king of the herd, replacing Sampson who, a time ago, went to the butcher at a goodly price, although by no means fatted to the weight he might have been. This is a very handsome, dark-coloured bull, with a capital head and horn and a fine frame and, in looking at him, we can quite think that the breed was at one time a favourite one with graziers, for there is every indication of a good feeding bullock about him and, on the other hand, with his curly front and rough, bison-like mane, he is certainly a grand-looking animal to have about a gentleman's place, although we fancy that it is quite as well for strangers that he has a house and well walled-in yard allotted as his domain for, though the herdsman says he would do nothing except in play, he looks as if he was capable of playing somewhat roughly if he liked.

Some weaners in a close, hard by, next engaged our attention and amongst them a very promising cross between the Shorthorn and the Alderney; while amongst the young calves they have one crossed between the Long and Shorthorn, marked exactly like the Chillingham cattle, white with chestnut ears.

Perhaps the prettiest sight of the day was the dairy itself, with its cool, clean-looking stone shelves, glass milk pans, and such a collection of curious ware ranged round the walls as could scarcely been seen together elsewhere, while it is shaded from the sun by a chestnut tree so large that the limbs have to be supported by props. A walk by the pretty elm-shaded church which stands in the middle of the park brought us to the yard where the deer are fed with their hay and a stroll thence to the farm showed us some more very useful heifers and these, with the exception of a fatting beast or two at some outlying buildings, who are doing well, completed our Longhorn survey of Calke and ended as pleasant a stroll amongst the stock as it was ever our lot to enjoy.

At one time Sir John was a breeder of pedigree Shorthorns but about ten years ago he sold them off and made up his herd of Longhorns of which he had always kept a few. With the exception of not feeding quite so quickly as their more fashionable rivals, they have earned a capital character as useful beasts and we hear that when well made out, the butchers are very fond of them, for they always die as good as they look, and show a preponderance of capital lean meat. For those who wish to combine ornament with usefulness, the Longhorn is certainly a capital beast, and we are in no way surprised that though nearly expelled from the homestead of the tenant they are yet found lingering in more aristocratic precincts.

(*Augeas*)

*Longhorns in Calke Park ca. 1870.*

In an address given by Sir John Harpur-Crewe in 1876, to the tenancy and yeomanry cavalry on the arrival back at the Abbey of his son Vauncey and his new bride from their honeymoon, the great pride and depth of feeling he had for his animals is tangible. 'Perhaps you will allow me to add that if, after you have viewed all the beautiful presents which the bride and groom have received, and anything else which may be worth looking at in the house, any of you who would like to see my herd of Longhorn cattle, I shall have great pleasure in showing them to you, and I will meet you in the dairy yard for that purpose when I venture to think you will find me somewhat more in my natural element.'

This having been said, it was met with great cheers from the assembled company. It can be imagined that this will strike a chord with the sentiments of many proud Longhorn owners who, like Sir John on that day in 1876, could not wait to shrug off the fetters of the day and to stand once more at peace, surrounded by these majestic cattle.

Sir John kept a scrapbook of press clippings relating to all matters Longhorn, reports of sales, of shows and of articles on Bakewell. This scrapbook was finished by his son, Sir Vauncey after the death of his father in 1886, with the report of the sale of the Calke Abbey herd and the reduction of the flock of Portlands. Sir John had left instructions in his will that on his death his beloved herd of Longhorns was to be dispersed, as his son did not share his passion for agriculture and he knew that the estate would revert back to its former sporting ways. Sir Vauncey's all-consuming interest was birds, both alive and dead, and he was to go on to form one of the largest collections of taxidermy in the country, amounting to several thousand cases. He was rarely to be seen without a gun and became a virtual recluse. So Sir John had been wise in his decision, giving other Longhorn enthusiasts an opportunity to make use of his valuable bloodlines and not leaving the herd to deteriorate in the hands of his disinterested son and heir.

The following description is taken from a press clipping in the scrapbook. It comes from *Bell's Weekly Messenger* and was written by Joseph Darby, after the death of Sir John but before the sale. The report on the Portland sheep is included.

> Among the ancestral homes of our principal landed gentry Calke Abbey, the abode of the late lamented Sir J. Harpur-Crewe, is possessed of features of great interest, and the deceased baronet not only filled the spacious mansion with art treasures, including a collection of rare bird specimens, calculated to feast the eyes of any naturalist, but took great delight in the arts of agriculture and stock breeding.
>
> In the magnificent undulating park not only were to be seen

old and beautiful trees and immense herds of red and fallow deer but also Portland sheep and Longhorn cattle, both of which breeds he brought to a great height of perfection. In his patronage of the Portlanders the later Sir J. Harpur-Crewe may be said to have stood alone, and to him must be accorded the high honour of having preserved Portland sheep from the fate which overtook the old Berkshire, Norfolk, Mendip and many a once famous breed. Portland sheep are to be found today nowhere in perfection, but at Calke Abbey. In their native island, they have been so neglected as to have become not only few in number but indifferent in character.

On the contrary, the large flocks, numbering altogether nearly 400, which have so striking an appearance in the park of Calke Abbey, and which will be offered at public auction there by Messrs German, German and Cooper (who have sold them for many years at their sales at Ashby, realising from 1s to 1s 3d per lb) on the 19th May next year, display such meritorious characteristics no less than a pleasing appearance that it may naturally be expected, they may attract the admiration and regard of some of our nobility and country gentry, who will have a noble opportunity at the auction to possess themselves of a few of the ewes for propagation.

No prettier animal can be a denizen of a park. They have short, thick, rotund bodies on short legs like the best-bred Exmoors but are far less wild. In this respect they have most likely altered their original character by having been domesticated for so many generations in this good district. At any rate it has enabled them to attain larger size and greater weight of carcase than they are originally reputed to possess in the Isle of Portland. The sheep were brought direct from the Island of Portland by Sir Harry Harpur in the year 1770, who was ancestor of Sir John Harpur Crewe and the tradition is that they are descended from a few hapless animals which were cast ashore there, when the Spanish Armada was demolished in good Queen Bess's glorious days. Though their flesh is so excellent, they are not a dainty sheep; on the contrary, they are very hardy and will do well on scanty pastures.

The deceased baronet also brought his magnificent herd of Longhorns to very great perfection, and as the whole of it will be offered by public auction by Messrs Lythall, Mansell and Walters on Wednesday 19 May 1886, a description of it may be useful to those who think that the world should not be parcelled out entirely of one pattern, and that Bakewell's favourite breed may even now, in many respects, hold its own against the widely popular Shorthorns. The latter may, perhaps, come to earlier maturity, but, if so, that is the only superiority; as for hardihood, constitutional vigour and longevity few British breeds can equal the Longhorn. The distinguishing feature of the herd at Calke is its uniformity in high quality. It would be difficult to find in England so many animals of the breed brought to so high a standard of perfection, with noble, picturesque heads; a large proportion with tapering wheel-horns, encircling the neck itself.

The colour is a dark handsome brindle or red, with a sheet of white all down the back and white spots on the thighs. They are also well ribbed and mostly deep and compact in form, with a quality of skin and flesh a grazier would certainly not despise. The high standard for excellence for which the herd is so remarkable is only what might be expected considering that it was formed in the first place by the best strains possible to be obtained; that it has been maintained with such persistent care, skill and good management is qualified by the many prizes obtained from the showyard.

Some very grandly-shaped pure-bred oxen and steers of the Longhorn breed are also to be sold, which will afford an admirable opportunity for graziers and exhibitors to get animals of the right stamp, fit to feed on for winning prizes at the leading fatstock shows of November and December.

The late Sir John's name was well known at Smithfield and Bingley Hall. In 1861 he showed a beast at Smithfield which took the gold medal as the best cow in the show of any breed. His Longhorns have beaten the Shorthorns at local county shows, Shorthorn men being the judges, and in 1864 his Longhorn was the greatest attraction at the London show. The head of the animal now adorns the entrance hall at Calke Abbey, along with many others of a remarkable character.* In 1875 Sir John exhibited at Bingley Hall a Longhorn ox, and in the whole show only two animals were as heavy at the same age, the £100 prize Hereford steer, 19 months older, weighing only 136 lb heavier. In ten years Sir John sent no fewer than 11 of the prize oxen in the class at Bingley Hall, twice standing first and second.

* Some very fine heads are preserved at Calke, in some cases the horns being nine feet from tip to tip, taking in the measurement of the skull.

*Sir John Crewe's pair of Longhorn steers, which took the first prize at Birmingham in 1868.*

So we come to the report of the sale itself. It is interesting to note that of the auctioneers who sold the herd on 19 May 1886, Mr John Lythall was the very first secretary of the Longhorn Society, and the family of Mr Walters was to become one of those that helped the breed to survive in later years, when numbers had fallen to a very vulnerable level.

The early pedigree cattle sales were great occasions. The following is an unidentified press clipping from the family scrapbook.

> The weather on Wednesday, though heavy clouds threatened in the morning, turned out beautifully fine, and there was a large attendance at the sale, large numbers of breeders or their agents travelling from a distance to be present. Most of the farmers, dealers and butchers from the district were also there. The sale was preceded by a luncheon in the riding school, of which some 500 or 600 partook, the reputation of the family for open-handed liberality being fully maintained. Mr H. Chandos-Pole-Gell, High Sheriff of Derbyshire, presided.

The writer then gives a list of all the gentlemen present whom he was able to identify. Of these, perhaps the most recognisable today are: Mr T. L. Prinsep, Mr Carswell (agent for Mr W. J. Legh,

Lyme Hall, Cheshire), Mr Oxley (agent for the Duke of Bucking-
ham), Mr Turnbull (agent for Mr Mundy, Markeaton), Mr John
Gretton (Drakelow), Mr Matthews (Foremark), Mr George F.
Brown, Mr Wragg (Ashby), Mr R. H. Chapman (steward), Mr
Sale (Smisby).

After luncheon, the chairman proposed a toast to 'the Queen',
followed by one for 'Success to the Sale'. He said all those
present knew the circumstances under which the Longhorns
were to be sold. They also knew the great interest Sir John had
taken for many years past in the breed of cattle. They would
agree with him [the speaker] that it must be very painful to his
successor to part with them, but they were left to be sold, and
they would be. Individually he had taken a very great interest in
the Longhorn breed – the breed of our forefathers long before
any other kind was known in the Midland counties. There was
no class of cattle more hardy and more useful in their way, but
owing to many circumstances their cultivation was confined to a
few, enthusiastic people.

He had been born and bred amongst them, his father having
been a Longhorn breeder all his life. He had often seen Sir John
Crewe's Longhorns in different parts of the country and he was
sure they would meet with the approbation of all present.
[Applause.] Unfortunately the times were not very good but he
would remind them that if they wanted to secure good
Longhorns they must not wait until times were good. They must
get them when the opportunity occurred, and such an
opportunity as this might not occur again – for many years.

He was pleased to see so many Longhorn breeders present
from different parts of England, and he was sure they did not
mean to go back without some of the plums in their charge. He
could only hope they would fix their minds on the same animals.
[Laughter.] There were two good men at a sale, the first and the
last bidder, and if they took pains to be the last, they were certain
to get what they wanted. [Laughter and Cheers.]

Mr Shaw, who had acted as confidential agent of Sir John
Crewe for many years, acknowledged the toast on behalf of the
family. He expressed the deep regret felt by Sir Vauncey at being
unable to attend the day's proceedings but felt that it was
impossible so soon after his father's death. He thanked the large
company for their presence, and Mr Pole-Gell for his kind
remarks. He asked his audience to understand the awkwardness of

his position. He felt gratification in meeting them but, on the other hand, the death of Sir John and the dispersion of the famous herd of Longhorns and the unique flock of Portland sheep made it a day rather for sadness than rejoicing. [Hear! hear!]

He spoke on the merits of Sir John saying that he was a thoughtful English Gentleman [applause] and was deeply interested in everything connected with his estates. He was on the most friendly terms with his tenantry, both rich and poor [applause], and sympathised with them, not only in their successes but in their troubles. Sir John was a man of very great observation, great judgement and great decision of character, and those were all qualities he brought to bear in breeding and rearing the splendid herd of Longhorns and fine flock of sheep which they would have the opportunity of purchasing that afternoon. He hoped that every gentleman would be satisfied with his purchases, and look back with pleasure to his attendance on that day. [Applause.] He concluded by proposing a toast to the chairman.

The company then adjourned to the sale rings at the dairy.

The sheep were sold first by Mr George German, who began by giving a brief history of the flock. First, 110 Portland ewes and 125 lambs were offered in 22 lots, the amount realised being £424 7s 6d. The top price was given by Major Burgess of Hendon who secured five ewes and 10 lambs for £25. Two similar lots made £23 15s and £22 10s respectively. The remainder were sold in lots of five ewes and five lambs. The price per ewe and lamb averaged £3 10s but where a ram lamb was included it rose to £4 12s 6d, the latter price being given by Mr J. German. Fat sheep went up to £3 7s, wethers went to £3 4s, ewes up to £3, paid by Mr Matthews of Foremark. Two Portland rams were £4 each, one going to Major Burgess.

At a quarter to three a move was made to the cattle ring where Mr Lythall took up the running. He said, valuable as was the flock of sheep which had been offered by Mr German, it was more as a breeder of Longhorns that the late Sir John Crewe's fame as an agriculturist was established. This was an opportunity which might not occur once in a century, and it should be taken advantage of by those who did not wish to see the oldest, most profitable and most picturesque breed of English cattle become extinct. All the animals had been out during winter and were not in any way prepared for sale.

Mr Lythall then commenced the sale, which took 2½ hours,

but was watched with unabated interest. Some of the prices obtained were exceedingly good, some of the bullocks making 8½d a pound, the top price of 44 guineas being given by Mr Shaw of Fradley for a splendid brindle and white ox, and the well-known dealer of Melbourne, Mr Toone, purchased the two best bulls, Cornet and Farmer, the sires of much of the young stock which were sold, for 35 guineas and 28 guineas respectively. Mr Watts of Melcombe took away a sound young animal, Robin Hood, for crossing, it is believed with Shorthorns, and Mr Bates of Malvern secured a gem in Little John. This gentleman was a large purchaser and paid the top price for calves, namely 14 guineas for a capital young heifer by Cornet called Cumberland Duchess which he secured after an exciting contest with Mr Bradley who was also a considerable buyer. Mr Griffiths secured a good young calf for the classic groves of Hawarden and Mr Oxley made several purchases for the Duke of Buckingham. Mr Carswell also secured a couple of heifers to join the celebrated herd at Lyme Park. The last animal on the catalogue was a yearling heifer, a cross between an Alderney and a Longhorn, supposed to be the only one in England. The experiment was purchased by Mr Matthews of Foremark for 12 guineas. The total figure for the cattle was £1,906 1s 6d, giving an average, including calves, of £19 1s 2½d.

## LONGHORN COWS AND HEIFERS

|  | Guineas |
|---|---|
| Trimmer 4th, calved 1876, by Peeping Tom | |
| Mr Morley, Derby | 20 |
| Brindle cow calf of above, by Cornet | |
| Mr Summerfield, Lichfield | 8 |
| [Lot here missing due to burn on the scrapbook.] | |
| Red & white cow calf of above, by Cornet | |
| Mr Hunt, Morley | 9½ |
| Dairymaid calved 1879, by Hardy | |
| Mr Wilkinson, Hartshorne | 24 |
| Cow calf of above, by Cornet | |
| Mr W. E. Gladstone | 6½ |
| Tulip 16th, calved 1876, by Old Time | |
| Mr A. O. Worthington | 20 |
| Lofty 2nd, calved 1869, by York | |
| Mr W. Sandiland, Ashby | 10½ |

Larkspur, 1878, by Earl of Upton 3rd
          Mr Morley, Derby                          16½
Heroine, calved 1877, by Lord Hardendale
          Mr J. German                              18
Tulip 24th, 1882, by Royal Duke of Upton 3rd
          Mr T. L. Prinsep                          25
Tiny 5th, 1882, by Duke of Upton 3rd
          Mr R. Hall, Thulston                       23½
Tulip 23rd, 1882, by Royal Duke of Upton 3rd
          Mr Thompson, Wilson                        20
Cow calf of above, by Cornet
          Duke of Buckinham                          8
Lofty 4th, calved 1879, by the Abbot of Calke
          Mr J. Summerfield                          16½
Brindle cow calf of above, by Earl of Moira
          Mr Bates, Malvern                          5½
Nymph, calved 1882, by May Duke
          Mr Watts, Melcombe, Dorset                 22
Sparkenhoe 3rd, calved 1880, by Marshal Neil
          Mr J. German                              26
Bull calf of above, by Cornet
          Mr J. German                              10
Lofty 5th, calved 1881, by Marshal Neil
          Mr Watson, Cumberland                      19½
Tulip 20th, 1881, by Marshal Neil
          Mr Eyke, Shrewsbury                        24
Canley 10th, 1881, by Harlequin
          Major Burgess, Hendon                      18½
Tulip 22nd, 1882, by Harlequin
          Mr Eyke, Shrewsbury                        25
Cumberland Duchess 6th, calved 13 May 1879,
   by Farwell
          Mr A. O. Worthington                       16½
Cumberland Duchess 5th, calved 6 May 1878,
   by Abbot of Calke
          Mr J. Summerfield                          19
Bull calf of above
          Mr Bates                                   14
Tulip 18th, calved 5 May 1878, by the Abbot of Calke
          Mr Wragg, Ashby                            17½
Tiny 4th, calved 1879, by the Abbot of Calke
          Mr J. German                              17½

Coquette, calved 1882, by Spondon
             Mr Watson, Cumberland        18
Honesty, calved 1882, by Spondon
             Mr J. German        15½
Brindle Beauty 2nd, calved 1 May 1882, by Royal
             Mr Hudson, Castle Donington        20½
Fanny 12th, calved 15 September 1881,
  by Marshal Neil
             Mr F. W. Symonds, Rugeley        19
Bull calf of above
             Mr Eardley, Market Drayton        4
Lovely 12th, calved 1883, by King of the Gypsies
             Duke of Buckingham        20
Brindle 7th, calved 1883, by Royal Duke of Upton 3rd
             Mr J. German        22
Lofty 6th, calved 1883, by Royal Duke of Upton 3rd
             Mr W. J. Leigh        23
Cumberland Duchess 8th, 1883, by Royal Duke
  of Upton 3rd
             Mr Prinsep        25
Upton Brindle Beauty, 1883, by May Duke
             Mr Watson, Cumberland        21½
Upton Queen, 1883, by May Duke
             Mr Bowley        27½
Speranza, 1883, by Royal Duke of Upton 3rd
             Mr Matthews, Foremark        19
Queen of Spain, 1884, by King of Gypsies
             Mr Matthews        19
Tinted Venus, 1884, by King of the Gypsies
             Mr W. J. Legh        19
Trifle, 1884, by Royal Duke of Upton 3rd
             Mr Bates        16
Gem, 1884, by Earl of Moira
             Duke of Buckingham        25
Diadem, 1885, by Earl of Moira
             Mr Worthington        22
Diamond, 1884, by Earl of Moira
             Mr Bates        16½
Castanette, 1885, by Exchange
             Mr Preston Coleorton        11½
Cow calf, by Cornet
             Mr Spencer, Derby        8½

Cow calf, by Cornet
                    Mr Summerfield                              7½

### BULLS

Cornet, calved 1882, by The Captain
                    Mr Toone, Melbourne                         35
Farmer, calved 1883, by Duke of Albany
                    Mr Toone                                    28
Nomad, calved 1884, by King of Gypsies
                    Mr Moorcroft, Burton                        25½
Robin Hood, calved 1885, by Earl of Huntingdon
                    Mr Watts, Melcombe                          25
Little John, calved 1885, by Earl of Huntingdon
                    Mr Bates                                    24½
Friar Tuck, calved 1885, by Cornet
                    Mr Causer, Shenstone                        10½
Blucher (property of Mr W. J. Matthews), calved
    1883, by Prior of Ashby
                    Mr R. Hall                                  12½

The top price for the day was the fat four-year-old ox by
the Abbot of Calke which went to Mr Shaw of Fradley, for
44 guineas.

Sir John died in 1886, and an agricultural correspondent of the
time wrote:

> The late Sir John Crewe's position as an agriculturist was quite
> unique in the Midlands and, in many respects, may be compared
> with Bakewell in Leicestershire, Bates in Yorkshire and Coke in
> Norfolk, for the great interest he took in improving all domestic
> animals. He loved, as the great breeders named did, to study their
> habits and improve their best characteristics. . . . Truly Calke
> Abbey and its surroundings may be termed 'classic ground' for
> domestic animals, and agriculture generally.

## The Duke of Buckingham's Longhorns at Stowe Park

Arriving at the quaint old town of Buckingham by train we had a
pleasant drive through the beautiful avenue which leads from the

town to Stowe Park and which, after a mile and three quarters, brought us to the hospitable roof of Messrs Oxley who are the Duke's agents and in whose hands is placed the keeping of the Longhorn herd. How well the trust has been carried out our subsequent remarks, as well as the long lists of prizes that have been won, will show.

We were shown to the yard where the herdsman soon led out the grand bull Conqueror the third, the Birmingham RASE winner, for us to renew our acquaintanceship with. A magnificent specimen of the breed and, as we look over him, we can well understand how it is that he has never been beaten. He has a fine head, beautiful neck, short legs, carcase as straight as a gun barrel, good quarters and is a rich brindled colour shading off lighter towards the quarters, and shows all the orthodox markings of the breed. He is by Young Conqueror, a son of Old Conqueror, and out of a cow of the breed of Mr Twycross of Canley. He came out as jauntily as ever and, having been let down a bit from showyard condition is, we hear, as good in service as ever he was in his life and, since we saw him, has again taken first honours at the Royal, at Liverpool.

Leaving him, we came on Wild Rose, a very beautiful in-calf cow. Her head and horn are capital, she has a back on which you could make up a bed, and is altogether a very beautiful animal. Moreover, she is well worth consideration as an example of the aptitude of the Longhorn race for quick feeding, as we were informed by Messrs Oxley that she had been got into show condition for the Royal at Liverpool within a very short time, and had been in low condition previously. When we saw her many a butcher would have been glad to have the chance of driving her to the slaughterhouse. She was second at the recent Royal Show.

Our attention was next turned to quite a juvenile, a bull calf by Conqueror III out of a heifer that took second prize at Birmingham, and a smarter one for his age than Young Sambo, as we believe he is to be called, is seldom seen. He is very level and true made all over, and a capital colour. With him also was White Rose's calf, another very neat one.

A couple of heifers next claimed our attention and, of them, Waterloo, a nice useful beast by the old bull, particularly good behind, looks altogether like framing into a prize taker. Next to them was Earl of Temple by Conqueror III out of Duchess, never yet exhibited. He has not been sent along and forced as some of

*Conqueror 3rd, bred by the Duke of Buckingham and Chandos and winner of first prizes at RASE shows in 1876, 1877 and 1878.*

the rest have and consequently he is not so shapely in appearance, while he is somewhat coarser in the head. There is no doubt that he is a very useful bull but we are inclined to doubt whether he will ever show the grand quality of his sire, even if he is made up for show.

The Marquis, a first-prize taker at Birmingham, took our eye much more. He was two years old on 27th March, and certainly has made capital use of his time while he has been in the world. He has a rare loin, is good in colour, shows a deep forehand, has a powerful set of thighs and quarters on short legs, and altogether struck us as one of those thick, deep fleshed animals that are sure to come out quite as good as they look and prove well to the butcher, while the great amount of quality he shows tells at once that he must be a good feeder.

In a small paddock close by was what we took to be the gem of the herd, Countess of Temple, a daughter of the old bull who also took a first at Birmingham. Many are the animals of various breeds we have run our eyes over, Shorthorns, Herefords, Devons, Sussex, etc., but we have never seen to our mind a more beautiful beast than this Longhorn heifer. For depth and squareness of frame no Shorthorn could beat her and, for horn, countenance and quality, she is not to be surpassed. We saw her just at her best and, when shown at Liverpool where she obtained a second prize, she was too near her time of calving to show to anything like the same advantage, as the bloom was considerably gone off. With her was another heifer out of a cow of Mr Godfrey's who took a prize at Wolverhampton, called Buttercup II, and an undoubtedly good beast she was but, as we told Mr Oxley, she should not have been seen at the same time as Countess of Temple, for that heifer so filled the eye that it was impossible to turn to anything else when she was present.

A bull bought from Mr Godfrey and called Earl of Wigston is higher on the leg, plainer in the quarters and shows less quality than the home-bred ones, but no doubt he will answer a good purpose in introducing a change of blood. A nice lot of calves, of capital colour and good strains of blood, completed our inspection of the home premises before we started for the Park to see the herd of cows.

Here, as we turned to the wide expanse of greensward, and saw the mothers of the herd spread out and grazing quietly over its slopes, the picturesque characteristics of the Longhorn came out in all their beauty and it was impossible to help feeling that there is no breed of cattle which so well becomes a nobleman's park at the Longhorn, for nothing can equal their grand dignity and stateliness.

First we saw the heifer Lady May, own sister to Countess of Temple, but at the time of our visit she was by no means looking her best. Then there was her dam, a fine finch-coloured cow that had taken a second at Wolverhampton. Lady Twycross, first at Birmingham, came forward as if anxious that her showyard honours should not pass unnoticed, but it was in vain as far as commendations on our part were concerned, for the Messrs Oxley prefer the 2nd to her on that occasion, Barmaid, an opinion in which we concur, as did a great many good judges who saw them in the Royal enclosure.

Baroness, a very good dark red cow, then caught our eye, 'neat as paint' as the saying is, notwithstanding she had roughed it all winter, a thing which tells little on this hardy race. Then there was her dam, Lady Caroline, a fine old cow of the same colour, who took a second prize at Oxford. Wildfire, dam of Wild Rose, and The Marquis, was pointed out to us as one of the cracks of the herd and, pointing to Emma, a rare dark brindle, Mr Oxley remarked: 'We would like to get them all of that colour.' Then we strolled away across the hill towards the great house and into what are called the pleasure grounds.

This is an area of 300 acres where cedars and other trees of extraordinary dimensions are to be seen. It is an area quite distinct from the park and appears to be a veritable forest. Within this area one might well fancy from the number of temples which are erected, that one had been transported to Greece and that the whole heathen mythology had dropped their temples in this chosen spot. Not that I would for one moment insinuate that the noble owner of Stowe and his ancestors are, or have been, given to Pagan rites, but that no expense has been spared in decorating these extensive grounds. In fact, some new view with a temple or grotto is continually opening on you, while the screams of the peacocks, which run wild here, would lead us to believe that Juno was the presiding goddess and that Argus (fabled to have 100 eyes) was kept here on guard to watch the movements of Io (loved by Zeus and changed by Hera, wife of Zeus, into a cow) in the shape of a Longhorn heifer in the pastures beyond. Then as we wandered through the whole coppices of choice shrubs, suddenly we came on a secluded little valley low down amongst the wood-covered hills where grazed a lot of choice young Longhorns. Strange sight, perhaps, but as we listened to the old herdsman's recital of the merits of the place, we no longer wondered that the descendants of Lady Caroline, the Buttercups and the Primulas were here, for we found it was the best place for wintering young stock to be had, and far before the yards and sheds for health. Here our task was done, and returning through the pleasure grounds, hares scudded away from under our feet as we made our way to Messrs Oxleys' hospitable roof. After draining a stirrup cup we started once more for Buckingham. So we finished our inspection and a very pleasant day altogether, coming away with the impression that, although Messrs Oxley have not very long held their present post, the herd has fallen into hands that will do it justice, as well as with the conviction that we never saw so much quality in Longhorns before.

*(From a Calke Abbey scrapbook, provenance unknown)*

# CHAPTER ELEVEN

# Breed Recognition

## The Longhorn Cattle Society

In December 1875, a meeting was held in Bingley Hall, during the Birmingham Fatstock Show, with the intention of starting a Longhorn Cattle Society and a herd book. Mr T. L. Prinsep of Croxall presided, and a good number of breeders were present, amongst whom were Col. Dyot, MP, Mr W. P. Cox, Mr Oxley (for the Duke of Buckingham), Mr Townley Parker, Mr R. H. Chapman, Mr J. Godfrey, Mr T. Satchwell, Mr Taverner and many others.

The chairman said he could bear evidence to the worth of the breed for, having tried it, he was perfectly surprised at the produce they gave. 'Devonshire cream could be as well made in Derbyshire as in the West Country,' he said. He moved: 'That in consequence of the increasing interest manifested in Longhorns, and with the view of securing this old-established breed in its proper position amongst English Cattle, this meeting is of the opinion that it is desirable to form a Longhorn society.'

This was seconded by Mr T. Satchwell whose herd had been in existence for three generations, having been started by his grandfather.

Mr Townley Parker then moved: 'That believing in purity of blood, breed is essential to improvement, this meeting is further of the opinion that the pedigrees of Longhorns should be duly recorded, which object will be best obtained by establishing a Longhorn herd book.'

Mr Forrest proposed, and Mr Taverner seconded, a third resolution appointing a committee, consisting of Sir J. H. Crewe,

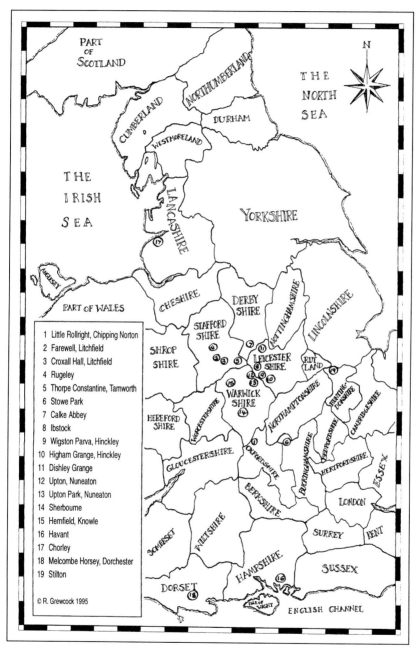

1 Little Rollright, Chipping Norton
2 Farewell, Litchfield
3 Croxall Hall, Litchfield
4 Rugeley
5 Thorpe Constantine, Tamworth
6 Stowe Park
7 Calke Abbey
8 Ibstock
9 Wigston Parva, Hinckley
10 Higham Grange, Hinckley
11 Dishley Grange
12 Upton, Nuneaton
13 Upton Park, Nuneaton
14 Sherbourne
15 Hemfield, Knowle
16 Havant
17 Chorley
18 Melcombe Horsey, Dorchester
19 Stilton

© R. Grewcock 1995

*Homes of some of the legendary Longhorn herds. Note the concentration in the Midland counties.*

bart, Mr W. T. Cox, Mr T. Levett Prinsep, Mr J. H. Burbery, Mr Townley Parker, Mr R. H. Chapman and Mr J. T. Oxley, to consider and report to a general meeting to be held at Birmingham during the Royal Show week in 1876.

The men responsible for the formation of the society were mostly from families who had supported the breed for generations. For example, Mr S. Forrest and Mr J. H. Burbery were nephew and uncle, Mr Burbery, on his retirement, having put his Wroxhall herd, which was started by his ancestor Mr Jackson in 1750, into the hands of his nephew for safekeeping.

The Birmingham Royal Show in 1876 provided a great boost for the breed, as there was an entry of 60 Longhorns (see Appendix 1). The following article shows the resurgence of interest in the breed at this time.

## Mr John Godfrey's Longhorns

Being in Leicestershire shortly after the unusual number of more than three score Longhorns at the Royal Show at Birmingham, I paid my respects to the breeders in this county who were placed first. At Stoke Golding, where the church spire rises in the midst of many pastures and a few arable fields, we pulled up for an hour in driving from the station at the comfortable farmhouse of Mr Berry. A mixed herd of Shorthorns and Longhorns was feeding in the cool evening in pastures before the windows, unconscious of any rivalry, past, present or to come, between their races, but not unconscious of short commons this season in consequence of the drought. I have seen no pampering of cattle in Leicestershire nor was there any here. When the pastures run short of grass the cattle suffer. You may order linseed cake as Mr Berry told me he did for the cattle last year, and presently things are not quite right in the cheese room. You may manipulate as usual with all possible and prudent care, and paste peppered paper over the cracks when the cheese rises and its skin breaks, but you cannot escape the effects of such a season as the present. If you feed your cows artificially your cheese will be the worse for it, and if you do not feed them your cows will be so. I have never seen such bare ribs in Leicestershire as now. On arrival, being unaware of the state of the pastures, I remarked of one herd I had seen before, 'Why, I thought your cows were bigger!' 'So they were,' was the short reply. I found the ribs of this dairy as distinct as the keys of a piano; and the point of my stick passed along them produced sounds far too bony to be pleasant. Heavy rains are sadly wanted. Longhorns pick up rapidly in good grass and they are hardy and can rough it well in winter as the thick hides and coarse limbs of the common sort would indicate. The merits of the breed have been summed up concisely, Mr Berry showed me some animals of excellent quality: and I then passed on to visit next day a herd with no Shorthorns alongside, placing it, as it were, on trial.

Mr John Godfrey of Little Wigston Farm, near Hinkley, owns, rents and occupies 120 acres of pasture and meadow and 20 acres of arable land, all for sale at the present time, worth from 50s to 60s to rent, and worth as grass 25 per cent more than as arable. The soil is a good sand loam with water-worn pebbles in it, a drift geologically covering the New Red Sandstone strata on which it rests to a considerable depth. The meadows are on the banks of a little stream running through a disproportionately wide valley into the Soar – one of the few rivers of Leicestershire – below the farm. The holly and yew have grown upon the farm immemorially and may still remain about the hedges and in clumps and rows here and there, supplying with other trees, that ample blind which I must say is very pretty in this part of the country, though it must cost the occupiers of the land a great deal annually to maintain it. The elm is, however, the prevailing tree and in Brick Kiln Close a pasture of 8 or 9 acres we found 20 cows and a bull beneath the shade of a hedgerow of stately English elms growing to a great height on the rich loamy soil. Here was the best blood of Dishley Grange, which can be traced through the herds of Chapman of Upton, Green of Odston and other eminent breeders. This best blood has lately flowed direct from Mr Godfrey's herd to that of the Duke of Buckingham and Chandos, the winner of the 1st prizes for bulls in the two classes at Birmingham, and to that of Mr Satchwell who was commended in two instances for cows, and of Messrs Burbery, Chapman, and others.

The natural colours of a Longhorn are black, red and white. The sides and head are brindled by the admixture of the black and red, or they may be red only (pale or deep) but the back is always white. The bull which might be observed dallying with a wanton heifer in this secluded pasture, on the cool north side of a hedge, is as dark on the sides as a lion. Old Brindled Beauty, a grand cow, grazing near him is almost as dark. Fairy is a rich deep red without black, and Wide Horn is equally perfect and a pale red. These are cows of long descent, and of a beauty which has captivated the professional and public eye more than once. Fairy's deep, large frame is perfection. She is descended from the 'Sampson' breed, and won the 1st prize at the Warwickshire show in 1873. Wide Horn is no less famous. She comes towards us swaying in her walk, a barge of beef on legs, not too stout, carrying her prodigious horns low, and stretched across the grass, 66 in. from tip to tip. She is a beautiful cow, pale red upon the sides and without a black hair on her. Brunette, her daughter, a 3 yr old, with her first calf, and all the promise of a milker in her square well formed bag, shows a perfect breeding with a brindled coat and soft skin.

There are others which might be mentioned, and, in fact, there is not a cow that might not be sketched as a good specimen of the breed, but I must here finish with the Last Rose of Summer, sister to the Duke of Buckingham's First Conqueror, bred by Mr Godfry. She has the slightly Roman nose which is proper in this breed, the horns of a great length, firm in texture, placed low on the skull, nicely sloping in perfect character, and particularly fine from head to point. May her horns be exalted some day to their deserved position in some breeder's hall. There are at least a dozen pair of horns in this herd worth polishing, and there is not a coarse horn in the lot.

We found Tiger, the 2nd prize Young Bull at Birmingham, in a suitable lair, an animal with all the colours and with the spotted thighs which denote purity of breeding. He has the admired Roman nose, and I should have estimated the present weight of beef of this 12-month-old bull at 75 stone, worth £22 10s at 9d per lb. or 9s per week from birth. The owner thinks this under the mark, and it may be so, but what a great return it is! If the feeders of common stock would take these figures to bed with them and meditate upon them, and compare them with such returns as they get from common cattle, our fairs and markets would soon be swept of their rubbish. Length of frame is the boast of the Longhorn breed.

There are, at present, 21 cows on the farm, four two-year-old heifers, four yearlings, and eight calves. About 3 tons of cheese is made in an average season. Profits have been reduced by the Foot and Mouth disease. Mr Godfrey agrees with Mr Berry as to the cheese going wrong when the cows receive artificial food.

(*H. Evershed, published 14 September 1876*)

# Herd Book

In the early days of showing livestock, it was the animal which counted – not the breed. Hence there were no separate classes for breeds which, in modern terms, would have been difficult to arrange before most breed societies and their herd books had been established. The first volume of *Coates Herd Book for Shorthorns* appeared in 1822, and other breed herd books were not started until the 1870s.

As a result of the general meeting called to form the society, the first volume of the herd book was published in 1878. It had a preface by Mr John B. Lythall, the honorary secretary appointed to the new society, who had obviously gone to enormous trouble to research the history of the breed and to record important sales of the previous 45 years. Lythall is the same man who conducted the sale of Sir John Harpur-Crewe's Longhorns in 1886.

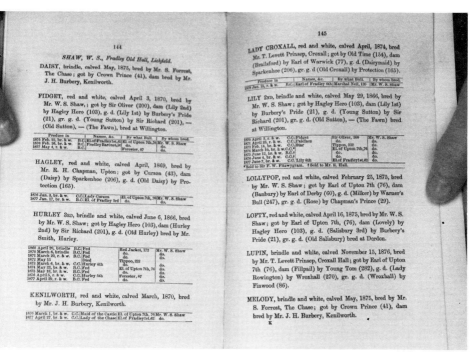

*A page from the first Longhorn herd book, published in 1878.*

Details laid down for the new society were a subscription of one guinea per year, a registration fee for bulls of 5s, for cows of 2s 6d and for calves of 2s 6d. Non-members were charged £1 to register bulls and 10s to register cows, and £1 for the herd book.

The first herd book of the society, published in dark navy leather with gold lettering in 1878, announced:

President – His Grace the Duke of Buckingham and Chandos.

Vice-presidents – Sir John H. Crewe, Bt, Major General Sir F. Fitzwygram, Bt, W. J. Legh Esq., MP, G. F. Muntz Esq., and T. L. Prinsep Esq.

Treasurer – Mr Joseph H. Burbery.

Committee –    Mr W. P. Burbery    Mr J. T. Oxley
               Mr R. H. Chapman   Mr T. Satchwell
               Mr S. Forrest       Mr W. S. Shaw
               Mr J. Godfrey       Mr V. B. Watts
               Mr R. Hall.

Hon. Secretary – John B. Lythall.

Herd books have been published as follows:

Vol. 1 – 1878, Vol. 2 – 1899, Vol. 3 – 1901, Vol. 4 – 1903, Vol. 5 – 1905, Vol. 6 – 1907, Vol. 7 – 1909, Vol. 8 – 1911, Vol. 9 – 1915, Vol. 10 – 1917, Vol. 11 – 1919, Vol. 12 – 1921, Vol. 13 – 1923, Vol. 14 – 1925, Vol. 15 – 1927, Vol. 16 – 1930, Vol. 17 – 1931, Vol. 18 – 1933, Vol. 19 – 1935, Vol. 20 – 1937, Vol. 21 – 1939, Vol. 22 – 1951, Vol. 23 – 1955, Vol. 24 – 1962, Vol. 25 – 1966, and from there to the present day.

Although the animals entered in the first herd book were not great in number, they consisted for the most part of some of the greatest blood the breed had ever possessed, coming as they did from the remnants of some of the purest and oldest herds in existence.

During the 1880s the breed took another dip in popularity, with most of the agricultural societies ceasing to have classes for the Longhorn. But by 1898 the tide turned once more in their favour, and the Birmingham Royal Show again opened its gates to the breed, stimulating the second herd book in 1899 and the revival of the Society. Several new herds were formed, and the Society was able to boast 21 members. This enthusiastic band of men, apart from keeping the spirit of the Longhorn alive in the show ring, pitted their skills in milking trials against other breeds. Amongst those taking part was Mr W. Hanson Sale of Arden Hill, the forebear of Mr Jim Beechey of the present Arden herd of Longhorns.

## Recent Years

The breed continued quietly until the Second World War, when it once again virtually disappeared. The Society ceased operation, and the breed itself was only kept alive by enthusiasts such as Messrs M. E. H. Walters, 'Grendon', W. E. Nokes, 'Hill', R. Wales, 'Stoke', and J. S. Stanhope of the 'Watling' herd, who re-formed the Society in 1948.

The Longhorn's finest hour to date in the show ring came at the RASE meeting in 1981 when the breed produced the winning pair to take the coveted 'Burke' Tropy against all other breeds, in the form of Eyebrook Richard, bred by the late Mr T. B. Johnson, and Rousham Carnation, bred by Mr C. Cottrell Dormer. This sparkling pair in the ownership of Mrs B. Weiner thrust the breed into the spotlight, since which time it has gone from strength to strength.

Today it has 392 members, 206 herds and a total of 2,500 breeding stock. The secretary is Elizabeth L. Henson of Peel House, 14 West Street, Shipston-on-Stour, Warwickshire CV36 4HD. Tel.: 01608 662 967. She is able to suggest members' herds which may be inspected.

## Longhorn Breed Standards

Standards for the Longhorn breed have, as with most breeds, varied down the years. The present Longhorn Cattle Society sets out the following standards:

> The HORNS to be fine in texture with traces of pink towards the base and free from any black coloration. The shape to come

either straight from the head with a forward sweep or turned with an incurve towards the mouth. Thick or coarse horns, or a tendency to grow backwards, are seen as undesirable.

The EYE to be prominent and of docile expression.

The BODY to be level in the back and well sprung over the ribs. The shoulder to be neat but full behind. The animal to be wide over the sirloin, level over the pins and to have a neatly set on tail. It should have a level underline, not be coarse in the brisket, be full in the thigh and lengthy and level in the steak piece and not split up between the hind legs. The cow to have a level, silky bag, well up under the tail, with teats well placed, of good size but not coarse.

The HIDE to be thick but soft to the touch and pliable.

The COLOUR is optional, but all to have a white line down the back, and with a slight preference given to red brindles and rich reds and to a white patch on each thigh. Cattle with black on the horns, black hooves or with no red hair in the coat are considered undesirable and are to be discouraged.

# Conclusion

So what, might you ask, does the Longhorn offer as we near the 21st century? The answer is, very much indeed. Animal welfare is under public scrutiny, more than at any other time in our history. With the call for less intensive and more extensive farming, an animal that can produce a large, lean carcase of high-quality beef, on a mainly roughage diet, and without the use of great quantities of high-cost concentrate, must surely have a great future. The breed is renowned for its docility, ease of calving and mothering abilities, all absolute necessities for the modern suckler herd, keeping man management at a minimum, and at complete variance to many of the modern continental breeds. The cows produce a high butterfat milk, ensuring speedy growth to their vigorous offspring, and their hardy nature means they can thrive outside all year round, cutting out housing costs and reducing the risk of respiratory and other ailments. The Longhorn bull used as a crossing sire on dairy heifers guarantees ease of calving, with resulting females making excellent sucklers.

The Longhorn has seen many changes in its long and chequered past. It has seen its rivals come and go! Its colour is now more uniform than ever before in its history. Once it ranged from black through to the palest roan, and even whole coloured animals, without the signature stripe or finch mark, made up quite a proportion of its number. Surely one of its greatest charms is that the whims and fancies of fashion will always be outwitted by this ancient race for, as all breeders know, no two animals mated repeatedly will ever produce consistent colouration in their offspring.

Will the Longhorn breed endure? Let us hope so, and also that it will find its own niche in our modern world. May the growing awareness of its many wonderful qualities ensure its survival in the current market place, enabling it to resist any future obstacles. May it constantly remind us of the debt we owe to that enlightened man Robert Bakewell and his fellow improvers, without whose legacy our country would not have held the lead in world agriculture at the time of its great awakening.

I will leave you with the thoughts of J. Neville Fitt from 1876, which are truly fitting for the present. 'The Longhorn has endured a long eclipse, but now there seems every indication that he is about once more to emerge from obscurity, and take his proper place amongst the magnificent breeds of cattle for which England is justly famous.'

*Dishley Grange
in 1994.*

*Bakewell's tombstone in the
ruins of Dishley Church – a
replacement on the wall, the
original stone broken below.*

*A sump hole built by
Bakewell for his
irrigation works at Dishley.*

*A pair of Longhorns, 1803, by John Boultbee (Iona Antiques, London).*

*Two Longhorn cows with a Hereford, ca. 1840, unknown artist (Iona Antiques, London).*

*Two Longhorn bulls, 1833, by E. M. Fox (Iona Antiques, London).*

London, Pub.ᵈ March 1 1802, by George Garrard, Agricultural Museum, 23. George St Hanover Sqʳ.

A FAT LONG HORNED OX,

Bred & fatted at Dishley Farm in Leicestershire, by Mᵣ Honyborn, Successor to the late celebrated Mᵣ Bakewell.

*A Longhorn ox, bred and fattened at Dishley Grange by Robert Honeybourne, Bakewell's nephew, painted by Garrard.*

*The Longhorn heifer Bandy, bred by T. Paget, painted by Garrard.*

Pub.ᵈ by G. Garrard 23 George St Hanover Sqʳ March 1 1806.

A FAT LONG HORNED HEIFER.

Called Bandy, from Mᵣ Padget's Stock. Fed by the Late Duke of Bedford

*Calke Abbey in 1880 by W. R. Woods. In the foreground, left to right: Abbot of Calke, calved 9 March 1876, and Canley 2nd, calved 11 March 1869. Back row, left to right: Tulip 10th, calved 8 April 1872; Lofty 2nd, calved 1 November 1869; Beauty 4th, calved 12 March 1873.*

W. R. Woods

*A fine head from the Calke herd, Beauty 4th.*

Head of Longhorn.

*Blue and white transfer plate, made between 1818 and 1824 by Charles Heathcote & Co., showing Longhorn cattle grazing in front of an unidentified country mansion.*

*Some Longhorns of today.*

*Blackbrook Diva, 1st Junior Heifer and Reserve Female Champion, and Westwinds Emma, 1st Senior Heifer, with stockman I. Davison at the Royal Show in 1994 (David Platt).*

# References

*Agricultural Gazette*, 1876.

T. Bewick, *A General History of Quadrupeds*, 3rd edition, 1792.

Betham-Edwards, M., *The Autobiography of Arthur Young*, 1898.

Boswell's *Treatise on Watering Meadows*, 4th edition, 1801.

Coleman, J. (ed.) *The Cattle of Britain*, a series of articles, 1875.

Culley, George, *Observations on Livestock*, 1786, 4th edition, 1807.

Daniell, T. and W., 'British Farm Animals', *Walkers Quarterly*, 1932.

Druid, The (Henry Hall Dixon, 1822–70), *Saddle and Sirloin*, n.d.

Ernle, Lord, *English Farming Past and Present*, 4th edition, 1927. (1st edition, 1912.)

Ernle, Lord, *The Land and Its People*, c. 1924.

*Farmer & Stockbreeder Yearbook*, 1902.

Fitt, J. Neville, 'Longhorn Cattle: Their History and Peculiarities', *Journal of RASE*, Vol. XII, Part II, 1876.

Fowler, Sale Catalogue.

W. Fream, *The Complete Grazier*, 14th edition, 1900.

Fussell, G. E., *James Ward RA, Animal Painter 1769–1859 and his England*, 1974.

Harpur-Crewe family records, Calke Abbey, unpublished.

Houseman, Wm (ed.) *Cattle Breeds and Their Management*, 1915.

Houseman, Wm, 'Robert Bakewell', *Journal of the Royal Agricultural Society of England*, Vol. V, Part 1, 1894.

Jones, Prof. C. Bryner, *Livestock of the Farm*, Vols I and II, 1920.

Lowe, David, *On the Domesticated Animals of the British Isles*, 1842.

Marshall, William, *The Rural Economy of the Midland Counties; including the management of livestock in Leicestershire and its environs*, Vols I and II, 1790.

Mingay, G. E. (ed.), *Arthur Young and His Times*, 1975.

Monk, John, *The Agriculture of Leicestershire*, 1794.

Orwin, C. S., *A History of English Farming*, 1949.

Orwin, C. S., *Johnson's England, Agriculture and Rural Life*, 1954.

Pawson, H. Cecil, *Robert Bakewell*, 1957.

Pitt, William, *General View of the Agriculture of the County of Stafford*, 1796.

Pitt, William, *General View of the Agriculture of the County of Leicester-shire, including a survey of the County of Rutland*, 1809.

RASE, Royal Show Catalogues, various dates.

RASE *Journal* (2nd Series), Vol. 12, Part II, No. XXIV, 1876.

RASE *Journal* (3rd Series), Vol. 5, Part I, No. 17, 1894.

Russell, Nicholas, *Like Engendering Like*, 1986.

Sheldon, J. P., *Dairy Farming, c.* 1883.

Trow-Smith, Robert, *A History of British Livestock to 1700*, 1957.

Trow-Smith, Robert, *A History of British Livestock, 1700–1900*, 1959.

Wallace, Robert, *Farm Livestock of Great Britain*, 5th edition, 1923.

Youatt, W., *Cattle, Their Breeds, Management and Diseases*, 1838.

Youatt, W., *Sheep, Their Breeds, Management and Diseases*, 1837.

Young, Arthur, *Annals of Agriculture*, especially Vols 6, 7 and 10, *c.* 1786–8.

Young, Arthur, *The Farmers Tour Through the East of England*, Vols I, II, III and IV, 1771.

Young, Arthur, *On the Husbandry of Three Celebrated British Farmers*, 1811.

# APPENDIX ONE

# Birmingham Royal Show, 1876

There were no separate classes for Longhorns at the Royal Show until the meeting at Windsor in 1851. Following is a complete list of entries in the Longhorn classes for 1876.

Class 81. Longhorn Bulls over 2 years

825. Thomas Taverner, Upton, Nuneaton, Leics. Royal Duke of Upton 1st, red, 4 years 3 months, bred by Mr Nicholas Taverner, Upton. s. Son of Earl of Upton. d. Damsel.

826. William Thomas Cox, Spondon Hall, Derby. Earl of Upton 6th, brindle and white, 4 years 3 months, bred by R. H. Chapman, St Asaph, Flint. s. Earl of Warwick. d. Countess of Warwickshire by Old Sparkenhoe.

827. W. T. Cox. Earl of Upton 5th, roan and white, 4 years 2 months, bred by Mr R. H. Chapman, St Asaph. s. Earl of Warwick. d. Lady Willscote by Old Cropredy.

1st Prize 828. Duke of Buckingham and Chandos, Stow Park, Buckingham. Conqueror 3rd, brindle and white, 4 years 11 months, bred by exhibitor. s. Young Conqueror. d. Lady.

3rd Prize 829. William Smith Shaw. Fradley Old Hall, Lichfield, Staffordshire. Earl of Upton 7th, light brindle, 4 years 3 months, bred by R. H. Chapman, St Asaph. s. Earl of Warwick. d. Lady Upton 73rd by Old Sparkenhoe.

2nd Prize 830. Frederick Tomlinson, Southwood, Ticknall, Derbyshire. Peeping Tom, brindled, 3 years 1 month, bred by Mr Whitacre, Warwickshire.

831. Thomas Satchwell, Hernfield, Knowle, Warwick. Forester, brindled red, 2 years 3 months, bred by exhibitor. s. Twist. d. Lady Arden by Rockingham.

832. Samuel Forest, The Chase, Kenilworth, Warwickshire. King Lupin, red and white, 3 years 3 months, bred by exhibitor. s. Crown Prince. d. Lupin.

833. Samuel Forest. Crown Prince, red and white, 6 years 3 months, bred by Mr J. H. Burbery, Montague House, Kenilworth. d. Daisy.

Class 82. Longhorn bull over one year, not over two years

834. William Thomas Cox, Spondon Hall, Derbyshire. Lorne 1st, brindle and white, 1 year 3 months, bred by exhibitor. s. Lord Lorne. d. Pallas by Curzon.

835. William Thomas Cox. Lorne 2nd, brindle and white, twin to above.

837. Duke of Buckingham and Chandos. Earl of Dadford, brindle, 1 year 2 months, bred by exhibitor. s. Earl of Upton 3rd. d. Rose by Earl of Warwick.

1st Prize
838. Duke of Buckingham. The Marquis, brindle and white, 1 year 3 months, bred by exhibitor. s. Conqueror 3rd. d. Wild Fire.

2nd Prize
839. John Godfrey, Wigston Parva, Hinckley, Leicestershire. Tiger, red and white, 1 year, bred by exhibitor. s. Blue Knight. d. Daisy by Shakespeare.

840. Thomas Satchwell, Hernfield, Knowle, Warwickshire. Warrior, brindle and white, 1 year 2 months, bred by exhibitor. s. Ranger. d. Cherry by Peeping Tom.

Class 83. Cows over three years

841. Richard Hall, Walton-on-Trent, Burton-on-Trent, Staffordshire. Longhorns 4th, red and white, 6 years

2 months, in milk, calved 15 May, bred by Mr John
Godfrey, Wigston Parva, Hinckley, Leics. s. The Stranger.
d. Longhorns 3rd.

842. Henry Parsons, Haselbury, Crewkerne, Somerset. Prolific,
brindle, 5 years 4 months, in milk, in calf, calved
24 January 1876, bred by Mr V. B. Watts, Melcombe
Horsey, Dorchester, Dorset.

843. John Spencer, Villers Hill, Kenilworth, Warwickshire.
Beauty, red and white, 4 years 1 month, in milk, bred by
the late William Bolton, Finwood, Rowington,
Henley-in-Arden, Warwickshire.

3rd    844. Thomas Satchwell. Rosemary, red and white, 3 years
Prize        2 months, in milk, calved 20 May 1876, bred by
exhibitor. s. Red Lion. d. Valentine by Monarch.

845. Thomas Satchwell. Lady Forest, red, 3 years 2 months, in
milk, calved 26 March 1876, bred by exhibitor. s. Red
Lion. d. Brindle Beauty by Peeping Tom.

846. Thomas Satchwell. Lady Arden, dark brindle and white,
9 years 3 months, in milk, in calf, calved 27 July 1875, bred
by exhibitor. s. Rockingham. d. Crump by Blue Bull.

2nd    847. Samuel Forest. Bluebell, brindle and white, 6 years
Prize        2 months, in milk, calved 25 February 1876, bred by Mr
J. H. Burbery. d. Bluebell.

1st    848. Samuel Forest. Lady, brindle and white, 6 years 3 months,
Prize        in milk, in calf, calved 22 October 1875, bred by Mr J. H.
Burbery. d. Beauty.

849. William Wheeler, Long Compton, Shipston-on-Soar,
Warwickshire. (No name given), 6 years 3 months, in
milk, in calf, calved 25 February 1876, bred by the late
J. Wheeler, Cropredy Lawn, Banbury, Oxfordshire.

Class 84. Heifer in milk or in calf, over two years, not
exceeding three years

850. William Thomas Cox, Spondon Hall, Derby. Mayflower,

brindle and white, 2 years 1 month, bred by exhibitor. s. Earl of Upton 5th. d. Pallas by Curzon.

851. Richard Hemming Chapman, The Roe, St Asaph, Flintshire. The Bulkington Rose, white and coloured, 2 years 4 months, in calf, bred by Mr T. Warner, Weston Hill, Bulkington, Rugby, Warwickshire. s. Hercules. d. Fairy by Messenger.

852. R. H. Chapman. Lady Weston, white and coloured, 2 years 2 months, in calf, bred by Mr T. Warner, Weston Hill. s. Hercules d. Lupin by Messenger.

2nd Prize 853. Duke of Buckingham and Chandos. 'Barmaid', brindle, 2 years 9 months, in calf, bred by exhibitor; s. Conqueror 3rd, d. Negress 2nd.

1st Prize 854. Duke of Buckingham and Chandos. 'Lady Twycross', red and white, 2 years 10 months, in calf, bred by exhibitor; s. Conqueror 3rd, d. Wildfire.

3rd Prize 855. Frederick Tomlinson, of Southwood, Ticknall. 'Lady Weston', red and white, 2 years 4 months, in calf, bred by Mr Weston.

856. Frederick Tomlinson, of Southwood, 'Loophorn 4th', strawberry, 2 years 2 months, in calf, bred by exhibitor; s. Conqueror, d. Loophorn by Duke.

857. John Godfrey, of Wigston Parva, Hinkley, Leics. 'Beauty', red and white, 2 years 10 months, in calf, bred by exhibitor; s. Shakespeare, d. Primrose by The Stranger.

858. John Godfrey, of Wigston Parva, 'Bashful', red and white, 2 years 10 months, in calf, bred by exhibitor, s. Shakespeare, d. The Plum by The Stranger.

859. Thomas Satchwell, Hernfield, 'Minnie', light red, 2 years 3 months, in calf, bred by exhibitor, s. Twist, d. Lady Bountiful by Rockingham.

860. Thomas Satchwell, 'Carrie', red, 2 years 2 months, in calf, bred by exhibitor, s. Twist, d. Cherry by Peeping Tom.

861. Samuel Forrest, The Chase, Kenilworth, 2 years 2 months, in calf, bred by exhibitor, s. Crown Prince d. Cowslip.

Class 85. Heifers not exceeding Two years old.

862. Henry Parsons, of Haselbury, Crewkerne, Somerset, 'Prodigy', brindle, 1 year 2 months.

863. Henry Parsons, 'Promise', light brindle, 1 year 1 month, bred by exhibitor, s. Earl of Upton 3rd, d. Rollright by Earl of Warwick.

2nd Prize 864. William Neale Berry, of Stoke Golding, Hinkley, Leics, 'Pride of the Park', brindle, 1 year 2 months, bred by Mr Nicholas Taverner, Upton Park, Nuneaton, s. Brindled Boy d. Beauty by Mr Chapman's Wild Bull.

865. William N. Berry, 'Young Strawberrys' Perfection', red and white, 1 year 1 month, bred by exhibitor, s. Brindled Boy, d. Young Strawberry 2nd by Upton Hero.

3rd Prize 866. William N. Berry, 'Weston's Farewell', red and white, 1 year 2 months, bred by exhibitor, s. Royal Duke of Upton 1st, d. Damsel by Upton Hero.

867. William Thomas Cox, Spondon Hall, Derby, 'Ellen', roan and white, 1 year 2 months, bred by exhibitor, s. Tippo, d. Beauty by Emperor.

868. Duke of Buckingham and Chandos, 'Baroness', red and white, 1 year 7 months, bred by exhibitor, s. Conqueror 3rd, d. Lady Caroline by Conqueror.

1st Prize 869. Duke of Buckingham and Chandos, 'Countess of Temple', brindle and white, 1 year 10 months, bred by exhibitor, s. Conqueror 3rd, d. Lady Mary by Young Conqueror.

870. William Peyton Burbery, The Crofts, Stratford-on-Avon, 'Dumpling 4th', brindle and white, 1 year 1 month, bred by exhibitor, s. Crown Prince, d. Dumpling 3rd.

871. Frederick Tomlinson, Southwood, 'Pet 5th', strawberry,

1 year, bred by exhibitor, s. Peeping Tom, d. Pet 2nd by Conqueror.

872. Frederick Tomlinson, 'Pet 7th', brindle, 1 year 1 month, bred by exhibitor, s. Peeping Tom, d. Pet 3rd, by Duke 3rd.

873. Thomas Satchwell, Hernfield, 'Forest Gem', red and little brindle, 11 months, bred by exhibitor, s. Romeo, d. Lady Arden by Rockingham.

874. Thomas Satchwell, 'Rosalind', red and white, 1 year 1 month, bred by exhibitor, s. Ranger, d. Rosamund by Bulky.

875. Thomas Satchwell, 'Bloom', dark brindle and white, 1 year 3 months, bred by exhibitor, s. Ranger, d. Blossom by Peeping Tom.

876. Samuel Forrest, brindle and white, 1 year 4 months, bred by exhibitor, s. Crown Prince, d. Sleepy.

877. Samuel Forrest, red and white, 1 year 3 months, bred by exhibitor, s. Crown Prince, d. Beauty.

As well as the entries listed Longhorns also competed in the mixed dairy classes.

# APPENDIX TWO

# Stilton Cheese

Pitt reported that although the Longhorns' chief use was as a beef animal, the county of Leicestershire produced many excellent milkers. He considered Leicestershire to be a considerable dairy county, and reported that around Hinkley, Bosworth, Appleby and Snareston many respectable dairy herds of Longhorn cows were to be found of between 12 and 25 cows each. The milk of the Longhorn being very rich, producing 6 per cent butterfat, meant it was favoured highly for cheese and butter manufacture. Indeed, it was said that 'Though you may skim a Shorthorn's milk with a feather, a mouse may run over the cream of a Longhorn without fear of falling through.'

Leicestershire in the late 1700s was celebrated for its Stilton cheese. The first person ever to produce this most famous of Leicestershire cheeses was Mrs Paulet of Wymondham, near Melton Mowbray, who was still living when Marshall toured the district in 1789. Mrs Paulet was a relation of an inn keeper who kept the 'Bell' at Stilton in Huntingdonshire, on the Great North Road from London to Edinburgh. She supplied his inn with her quality cheese, which was exceptionally well received by his customers who paid half-a-crown per lb for the experience, but not knowing where it came from, it became known as 'Stilton' cheese.

After a while the place of origin was discovered, and the art of production learnt by other women of the district, until it was being produced in almost every village in that part of Leicestershire and Rutland. A recipe of the time, given by Pitt was:

> Take the milk of seven cows, plus the cream (probably of the previous evening's milk). Heat a gallon of water to scalding hot,

and pour it on three or four handfuls of marigold flowers that have been bruised a little, then strain it into a tub to your milk and add some rennet, but not too much, to make it hard. Put the curd into a sieve to drain. It must not be broken at all, but as the whey runs from it, tie it up in a cloth, and let it stand for half an hour or more. Then pour cold water upon it, enough to cover it, and let it stand half an hour more. Then put half of it into a vat, six inches deep, and break the top of it a little to make it join with the other, then put the other half to it, and lay a half-hundredweight upon it, and let it stand for half an hour. Then turn it and put it in the press, and turn it into clean cloths every hour the day it is made. The next morning, salt it and let it lie in salt a night and a day. Keep in swathed tight till it begins to dry and coat, and keep it covered with a dry cloth a great while. The best time to make it is in August.

# APPENDIX THREE

# Horn Shapes and Uses

It is said that the age of a Longhorn can be determined by the circular ridges which are present on its horns, like a tree with its annual growth rings. Until the age of two, the horn is smooth, but at three years a circular ridge appears at the base of the horn and another ridge is added in each succeeding year. Hence, by counting the ridges and adding two, the age of an older animal can be judged with tolerable precision, unless the rings have been defaced or artificially removed by scraping or filing.

These main annual rings are not to be confused, however, with other smaller rings that are sometimes found at the root of the horn and which are an indication that an animal has been poorly fed at some stage of its growth. Poor nutrition or accidents during the formative stages are also frequently responsible for horns that are crooked and unsightly.

By the age of three years, there is often a distinct cone of horn at the extremity. This will be shed eventually, leaving a perfect horn tip underneath, and is no cause for concern.

The horn should be fine in texture and of a yellowish colour, often with traces of pink towards the base, almost as if it had been bruised. Any trace of black in the horns is discouraged as showing evidence of an outcross.

The preferred shape for the horns from the handler's point of view is what are termed bonnet or wheel horns, that is, those that turn with an incurve towards the mouth, rather like the strings of a lady's bonnet. Horns which come from the head with a forward sweep are also quite acceptable.

Of course that is the theory; in practice, horns may take many directions. Sometimes animals can be seen exhibiting one bonnet and one straight horn. The only undesirable direction is horns that grow backwards from the head, which give the animal a curiously windswept appearance.

During the golden age of the Longhorn in the 18th century, it was thought that climate and region had a great effect on the direction that the horns took, but, as the fashion for horned cattle declined, so did the need to explain what affected their shape. The reader can ponder the possible validity of these suggestions for horn size and shape as visits are made to various herds in different parts of the country.

It is now generally acknowledged that Robert Bakewell fixed the style of the bonnet horn. His need was almost certainly one of economy, for he housed up to 170 cattle during the winter and animals sporting the bonnet type of horn took up less room than those with straight horns, and caused less injury to their neighbours.

Bakewell was certainly wise in back-fencing his hedge, a practice which immensely irritated the agricultural writer Arthur Young because he considered it to be uneconomic. But to anyone who has experienced Longhorns and knows the immense pleasure they gain from thrashing their heads around in a good thick stretch of hawthorn, back-fencing is an essential part of Longhorn husbandry.

In Bakewell's time there was a fashion for training horns, either by an attachment on the top of the animal's head or by using hot irons. By the latter method, incredible shapes could be achieved as, for example, in the case of the Fat Longhorned Heifer called Bandy, bred by Mr Paget of Ibstock, Leicestershire, and drawn by George Garrard in 1806.

It is usual to find with ruminants that the male carries the grandest horns, but this is not the case with Longhorn cattle. The bull carries thick, strong but comparatively short horns while the cow has finer but much longer horns. The best horns of all are to be seen on the heads of castrated males or oxen; they are of incredible length and almost invariably curve in the bonnet fashion. The length of horn is no indication of the temper of the animal. The Longhorn is an exceptionally docile breed (although there can, of course, be difficulties with individual animals in particular situations). Overall, however, it may be the case that, in cattle those with the longest horns are those with the most placid natures.

The entrance hall of Calke Abbey is hung with the mounted heads of prize oxen, the size of which is quite breathtaking. The horns are of great interest being both longer and thicker than are normally to be seen today. Admittedly they are the heads of oxen, which do grow horns far larger than both bulls and cows, but might it be that during this period, when horn was used extensively in the comb, button and lantern industries, cattle were bred as much for their horn as for their meat? Alternatively, over the years, when numbers of the breed have fallen to perilous levels, and outside blood has been most surely used, have we lost a little of what were once truly immense horns?

The horn industry was based in the south Midlands, which was well placed to take advantage of products from the cattle for which the area was famous, the Longhorn.

The horn consists of two separate parts – an outer horny case and an inner conical-shaped substance which is something between hair and bone. In the manufacturing process, the two were separated by a sharp blow. The outer case was then cut into three sections: the part from the root of the horn being flattened and used for combs; the middle section, after flattening by heat, was oiled to improve its transparency and then split into thin wafers to form a substitute for glass in the lanterns of the poor; and the tip of the horn was used by manufacturers of knife handles, whips and buttons, amongst other things. The core of the horn was boiled down to provide fat for the soap industry and the unusable bony substance left behind was ground down and sold back to the farmer as fertiliser. Drinking horns were also widely used at one time and little salt cellars of plugged horn, perhaps from the tip of the horn, have been used well into the present century by at least some workmen who have expected meat on some days with their midday bread.

Horn was thus an important raw material for a number of growing industries at one stage in our history. Some of the 'buttons and baubles' which our early explorers are said to have used as payment for vast tracts of territory in the New World are quite likely to have come from Longhorn cattle. And hoof and horn meal was that vital product of early industry which benefited the land, and led to the development of the superphosphate industry.

# APPENDIX FOUR

# A Chronology

1725 ● ROBERT BAKEWELL BORN ON 23 MAY

1760 ● FIRST RAM LET BY BAKEWELL FOR 16S

1783 ● DISHLEY SOCIETY FORMED

1788 ● LEICESTER AGRICULTURAL SOCIETY FORMED

1795 ● BAKEWELL DIED ON 1 OCTOBER

1811 ● SALE OF THOMAS PRINSEP'S HERD AT CROXALL, DERBYSHIRE

1819 ● SIR GEORGE CREWE SUCCEEDED TO HIS INHERITANCE

1844 ● SIR JOHN CREWE SUCCEEDED HIS FATHER

1873 ● SALE OF MR CHAPMAN'S HERD AT UPTON

1876 ● SALE OF MR R. BROWN'S HERD, FAREWELL, AT LITCHFIELD

1878 ● FIRST VOLUME OF THE LONGHORN HERD BOOK PUBLISHED

1886 ● SALE OF CALKE HERD ON 19 MAY

1896 ● BAKEWELL'S CHAIR AND PORTRAIT GIVEN TO THE R.A.S.E.

# Livestock Artists of the 18th and 19th Centuries

Paintings of animals are considered to have been fairly faithful representations in the 18th century, before artists succumbed to the financial inducements of their patrons in the 19th century and produced 'likenesses' of animals that can hardly be accepted today. The development of photography from around 1850 has brought more recent paintings back into the believable world for the modern viewer.

A number of artists are of relevance to the Bakewell and Longhorn story.

## John Boultbee (1753–1812)

Sporting painter who is sometimes claimed to have entered the Royal Academy Schools in 1775, although there is no record there of his enrolment. The Boultbee family records show that he was a pupil of Sir Joshua Reynolds. Boultbee's patrons included the Lords Stamford and Egremont, Robert Bakewell himself, Richard Tattersall and Thomas Coke, later first Earl of Leicester.

## John Fernely, Senior (1782–1860)

Leicestershire-born sporting artist who showed great talent for painting when apprenticed as a wheelwright to his father. In 1801, the Duke of Rutland arranged for him to study under Ben Marshall for three years in London. Throughout the rest of

Fernely's life, Marshall retained a strong influence on his work. He had many patrons, including Robert, first Earl of Grosvenor, later first Marquis of Westminster. Works by Fernely can be seen at Calke Abbey.

## George Garrard (1760–1826)

A sporting artist, who studied at The Royal Academy and also with Sawrey Gilpin, who later became his father-in-law. He became famous for his anatomically accurate models of livestock and for his engravings.

## Thomas Weaver (1774–1843)

The son of a Shropshire farmer, he was said to have been a pupil of John Boultbee, and was famous for his livestock paintings. His patrons included Thomas Coke, first Earl of Leicester, and Viscount Anson. He painted the famous 'Ram Letting at Dishley'.

# Index

*Numbers in italics indicate illustrations*

# FARMING PRESS BOOKS & VIDEOS

Below is a sample of the wide range of agricultural and veterinary books and videos published by Farming Press. For more information or for a free illustrated catalogue of all our publications please contact:

**Farming Press & Videos, Wharfedale Road, Ipswich IP1 4LG, United Kingdom**
**Telephone (01473) 241122      Fax (01473) 240501**

### Farming Through the Ages    ROBERT TROW-SMITH
From the earliest times to World War II, an account of Britain's farming history built around a remarkable collection of pictures.

### The Horse in Husbandry    JONATHAN BROWN
Photographs of horses working on farms from 1890 to 1950, with an account of how they were managed.

### Harnessed to the Plough (VHS video)
ROGER & CHERYL CLARK with PAUL HEINEY
Roger and Cheryl Clark demonstrate a year of contemporary horse-drawn cultivations and harvesting on their Suffolk farm. Additional commentary by Paul Heiney.

### First Steps to the Furrow (VHS video)
ROGER & CHERYL CLARK with PAUL HEINEY
Shows how a two-year-old Suffolk horse is trained for farm work; also covers feeding, housing, grooming and general care.

### Farming with Steam (VHS video)
Shows how steam was used on the farm in threshing, ploughing and hauling and recalls the life of a traction engine driver.

### Tractors at Work    STUART GIBBARD
150 photographs spanning 1904–94 show a wide range of tractors on farms in Britain in many working situations.

Farming Press Books & Videos is part of the Morgan-Grampian Farming Press Group which publishes a range of farming magazines: *Arable Farming, Dairy Farmer, Farming News, Pig Farming, What's New in Farming.* For a specimen copy of any of these please contact the address above.